A STUDENT'S GUIDE TO

NATURE AND

HUMAN VALUES

Paula Farca

Cortney Holles

Shira Richman

Division of Liberal Arts and International Studies

Colorado School of Mines

HAYDEN
HM
McNEIL

Printed in the United States of America

10 9 8 7 6 5 4 3 2 1

ISBN 978-0-7380-3643-4

Hayden-McNeil Publishing
14903 Pilot Drive
Plymouth, MI 48170

MillerD 3643-4 F10

CONTENTS

Acknowledgements

We owe a special gratitude to the Nature and Human Values Coordinator, Dr. Dan Miller, who contributed several chapters to our book and helped us format it. This project was his vision, and we were proud to help it come to fruition. We also want to thank our colleagues who teach NHV for their feedback and enthusiastic support. Our students encouraged our project and offered us sample papers and valuable comments and for these, we are deeply grateful. We also thank our predecessors in the development and ongoing evaluation of the Nature and Human Values course: Carl Mitcham, Jon Leydens, and Jen Schneider.

—Paula, Cortney, and Shira

INTRODUCTION

The National Academy of Engineering has identified fourteen global Grand Challenges for engineering in the twenty-first century. They range from perfecting fusion energy to providing access to clean water, from restoring the urban infrastructure to securing cyberspace, from enhancing virtual reality to reverse-engineering the brain. (You can see the full list at http://www.engineeringchallenges.org/.)

Accomplishing these tasks will take inspired technical engineering, but, as the Academy recognizes, most will require abilities and knowledge beyond engineering. In the twenty-first century, engineers will have to deal with social, political, and environmental issues, with cultural and cross-cultural values, and with difficult moral questions.

The Academy also recognizes that engineers will be increasingly called upon to assume leadership roles. The time has passed when engineers could see themselves as simply as expert professionals with little responsibility beyond accomplishing the design task assigned them. Given their special knowledge and abilities, engineers must take an active part in the public debates about how, when, and if we should engineer the world. And any debate about what we *should* do is a debate about values, about which courses of action serves the good and which does not.

This is why Nature and Human Values is a required course at the Colorado School of Mines. It is a course about the ethics of engineering—both about the specific ethical obligations that engineers have as professionals and their broader moral, social, and environmental responsibilities. And it is a course helps engineers in training to engage effectively, primarily through writing, in the public discussions that will shape the world.

This book will do a number of things for you. It will guide you through the process of writing and revising papers for NHV. It will help you do research for the final paper. It will give you an overview of argumentation and help you understand the ethical theories described in lectures and seminar meetings.

Read the sections of this book as your instructor assigns them. Keep the book at hand for reference and review. The more you use this book, the better you'll do.

Welcome to NHV.

Dan Miller

Coordinator, Nature and Human Values
Lecturer, Liberal Arts and International Studies
Colorado School of Mines

Chapter 1. NATURE AND HUMAN VALUES

1. NAE, ABET, AND NHV

In 2004, the National Academy of Engineering released a report, *The Engineer of 2020: Visions of Engineering in the New Century*, written by working engineers and engineering professors. The report detailed the skills and abilities engineers will need in the coming century. While much of the report had to do with emerging technologies and advanced scientific knowledge, a large part of it dealt with matters that engineers in the past would have considered simply not part of their jobs.

For example, the report holds that, by 2020, engineers should be prepared to "assume leadership positions from which they can serve as positive influences in the making of public policy and in the administration of government and industry" [1, p. 50]. The report also asserts that engineers should be "leaders in the movement toward use of wise, informed, and economical sustainable development" and "are prepared to adapt to changes in global forces and trends and to ethically assist the world in creating a balance in the standard of living for developing and developed countries alike" [1, pp. 50-51]. Given the problems that engineering will be called on to solve and given the huge impact that engineering has on the natural and social worlds, engineers will have to look beyond specific design problems. They will have to do engineering within a larger context—the global context of environment and human society.

ABET is the organization that accredits engineering and applied science universities like the Colorado School of Mines. It is composed of practicing engineers and engineering educators. When an ABET team evaluates a university, it considers whether the curriculum prepares students in eleven specific areas. Many of these are what you would expect. Graduates of the school should be able to "apply knowledge of mathematics, science, and engineering" and "design and conduct experiments, as well as to analyze and interpret data" [2, p.3]. Graduates of schools like CSM should be able to "to identify, formulate, and solve engineering problems." Many of the outcomes criteria, however, go far beyond the ability to apply science and mathematics to a particular design problem.

In fact, five of the eleven criteria deal with the same matters addressed by the National Academy of Engineering. ABET holds that graduates of schools like CSM should have these understandings and abilities:

- an understanding of professional and ethical responsibility

- an ability to communicate effectively

- the broad education necessary to understand the impact of engineering solutions in a global, economic, environmental, and societal context

- a recognition of the need for, and an ability to engage in life-long learning

- a knowledge of contemporary issues [2, p.3]

All five of these outcomes criteria are related to this course, Nature and Human Values.

Both the National Academy of Engineering and ABET recognize that, in coming years, engineers will be called on to do more than they have in the past. Both organizations argue that, while engineers must be technically proficient, they will have to consider issues that engineers in previous centuries probably ignored. A contemporary civil engineer may have to consider, not just the optimal design for a new highway, but the need to provide ways in which migrating wildlife can go across—or under or above—the road. A mechanical engineer may be asked not simply to use a CAD/CAM program to design a new device but also to take into account the costs of transporting the raw material needed for manufacture and the environmental impact of extracting and processing that material.

NAE and ABET both hold that engineers should assume leadership roles in dealing with current issues and public policy. As social and environmental issues become more complex and pressing, engineers have the scientific ability to understand the problems—and perhaps make the issues clear to the broader public—as well as technical creativity to advance solutions. There may have been a time when engineers considered their job to be taking what other people asked them to do and doing it, whether those other people were political leaders or heads of government agencies or CEO's of corporations. There may have been a time, in other words, when engineers thought their work was primarily instrumental; they created what other people decided needed to be created.

If engineers of the twenty-first century are to be leaders and take an active part in making decisions, they need a broader education and more extensive abilities than engineers of previous centuries. For that reason, and because of the NAE and ABET recommendations, all CSM students are required to take Nature and Human Values.

At many universities, students take one or two semesters of composition. Universities know that the ability to write clear, readable, well organized, effective English prose is important in careers, in social and political life, in living a meaningful, examined life. NHV is first of all a course in writing. And professional engineers write. An engineering report will have charts, graphs, data calculations, equations, and schematics, but the majority of that report will be sentences. The more an engineer advances in his or her career, the more writing he or she will do. And if NAE and ABET are right, engineers will increasingly need to write, not just for clients or technical audiences, but for broader audiences.

NHV is also a course about making choices. It is a course about how to think about choices. Toward the beginning of the course, we will consider principles and problems in engineering ethics. What moral guidelines do engineers have? What ethical beliefs should they have? Confronted with an ethically difficult situation, how can engineers go about finding the right course of action and, perhaps more importantly, justifying that choice with a rational argument. It may seem that engineers would face fewer ethical dilemmas than, say, doctors or lawyers, but that's not the reality. Working engineers report that they are regularly faced with difficult ethical choices and that they have to struggle with them.

As the course progresses, we will move from engineering ethics narrowly conceived to the ethics of engineering in the larger context, in relation to the natural and social world. The course will ask you to consider such issues as engineering in a world of limited energy resources, the future of nuclear energy, resource distribution, and engineering cities. Toward the end of the course, you'll be asked to deal with debates at the cutting edge of engineering—whether to allow the genetic manipulation of plants, the genetic engineering of human beings themselves.

2. NUTS AND BOLTS

NHV has two components: lectures and seminar meetings. In the weekly lectures, faculty from the Division of Liberal Arts and International Studies and, in some cases, CSM faculty from other departments will speak to you in Metals Hall of the Green Center. These lectures will cover some of the topics mentioned earlier. Some will present important ethical concepts and lines of thought; most will present specific, debatable cases in engineering and environmental or social ethics.

The lectures are designed to raise questions, not to answer them. They intentionally raise controversial issues and lay out arguments on both—or several—sides of a debate. They often describe problems for which there are no easy solutions. In a complex world, simple answers are very hard to come by.

In the lectures, listen carefully, take notes, jot down important facts and ideas, record your own thoughts. Turn off all cell phones and other electronic devices. Do not use a laptop computer unless you have a special need to use one and your seminar instructor has given you permission. Don't chat with classmates; your whispers will be heard by others rows away and distract them. Give the lecturer the respect due to him or her. CSM is preparing you for the profession of engineering, so begin now to comport yourself professionally.

Two things happen in the seminars. First, the seminar meetings are the place to talk about the issues and problems set out in the lecture. The seminars ask for open and honest, possibly energetic, and, above all, polite and respectful debate. Say what you think. Be prepared to have your view challenged. Be prepared to defend your view with a rational argument. If you're not sure what your view is on an issue, go ahead and explain why you're uncertain.

Second, the seminars are where you'll work on writing. Your NHV instructor has significant experience in teaching writing. He or she will assign the major papers and evaluate them. The seminar instructor will also assign exercises designed to improve your writing. Your instructor also assigns your final grade for the course. Faculty who present the weekly lectures play an important role in the course, but the seminar teacher is the instructor of record for the course.

The three major papers, described in more detail in Chapter 8, are worth a total of 700 points out of a total possible 1000 points for the semester. (Point totals for individual NHV sections may not end up exactly at 1000 points, but they should be close.) Your NHV instructor apportions the remaining 300 points to shorter papers, exercises, and other assignments specific to your seminar. Your instructor will probably include scores for attendance and participation.

References

[1] National Academy of Engineering, *The Engineer of 2020: Visions of Engineering in the New Century.* Washington. D.C: The National Academies Press, 2004.

[2] ABET, *Criteria for Accrediting Engineering Programs.* Baltimore: ABET, 2009.

Chapter 2. ENGINEERS AND ETHICS

In normal conversation and writing, "morals" and "ethics" mean roughly the same thing. For philosophers, however, there is an important and useful distinction. Morals are the values that an individual possesses and upon which he or she acts. Morality is a general set of beliefs about the rightness and wrongness of actions that people carry with them. People gain their specific moral beliefs as a result of family upbringing, education in school or church, or influences of peers. The most significant source of moral values—and maybe the most troubling—is mass media: television, film, books, and now the internet. We usually think little about our moral beliefs; we most often simply believe that our morality is good, or maybe the best, and try to live up to it as well as we can. Most of the time, we do not reflect on our values, ask whether they are legitimate, or consider whether they have rational grounds.

When we do reflect on beliefs about right and wrong action, we move from morals to ethics. Ethics is the attempt to understand why certain actions are right and why certain actions are wrong; it is reasoning about morality. Ethics—sometimes called moral philosophy—asks basic (and, at the same time often very difficult) questions. Are there moral principles that can and should hold for all people in all cultures? Does a good action have to have good results? Can an action be right even if it leads to harm of some sort? Why *should* any person act morally when there may be advantages to acting immorally?

For some students, all talk of ethics is futile. They often feel that moral reflection somehow means an attack on their values, or they feel that personal morality is unchangeable, or they feel that ethics is a matter of individual preference, different from one person to the next and, therefore, not open to discussion.

In the first case, it is true that moral philosophy does ask us to examine our moral values and see if they have rational foundations. That process can be uncomfortable because we may in fact discover that some of our values may not stand the test of reason. We may discover that some values fail in certain situations. We may even find out that, in the process of moral debate, other values have stronger grounds than some of our own. In most cases, however, moral reflection means less changing our values than clarifying them. Actions we intuitively feel to be good we can now articulate *why* they are good.

The second view, which holds that personal morality is set in stone and unchangeable, is more difficult to counter. Usually, this is a gut-level, defensive reaction rather than a considered intellectual position. Moral beliefs can and do evolve as we grow. Moral beliefs can become stronger and more nuanced as we reflect on them. The two-thousand year tradition of religious and secular moral philosophy attests to that fact.

The third case, which amounts to "Different people have different values, just as different cultures do, and who's to say that one set of values is better than any other?" is moral relativism. For this view, morality is just a personal preference, like a fondness for pepperoni pizza, and statements of personal preference are not debatable. While I may prefer pepperoni, you may prefer sausage pizza, and there is no way to say that one preference is at all better or more right than the other. Individual preferences, for the most part, concern only ourselves; my liking for pepperoni pizza affects only me. Moral values, in contrast, have to do with other people and the public sphere. When I act on my values, my action touches others, and if I'm asked to justify my action, and if I'm a moral relativist, I have little to say. In the world of professional engineering, where human lives and safety are often at stake, moral relativism is not an option.

The ethical theories we'll look at below are not just exercises in academic philosophy. They are ways of thinking ethically. Some will provide means of rationally deciding on a course of action in a difficult situation, perhaps in a situation where moral principles seem to be in conflict. And they offer something more important. Sometimes, we have to do more than make an ethical decision; we often have to justify that decision to others after the fact. In some cases, we may have to involve others in making the decision. These ethical theories are ways of thinking about right action and of talking to others, before or after the fact, about right action.

1.   CONSEQUENTIALIST ETHICS

Consequentialism says that a moral action is defined by its results, by its consequences. Very simply, a good action has good results, and a bad action has bad results. Right actions bring about benefits for those involved; wrong actions cause harm for those involved. If an action might result in both good and bad consequences, then the good should outweigh the bad or be better than alternative courses of action.

You can find a version of consequentialist ethics in all cost-benefit analyses. Costs are, of course, not desirable but usually necessary, and benefits are obviously positive results. A cost-benefit analysis hopes to find the course of action that minimizes costs and maximizes benefits.

Consequentialist ethics appeals to common sense. It makes sense to say that good actions lead to good in the world, that bad actions cause harm in the short or long run. At the same time, consequentialism seems to make sense in a complex, highly technological world: for any course of action, calculate the probable goods and bads, and the moral course of action will then be clear and justifiable.

But how exactly do we go about weighing the good and bad that may result from a particular action? One answer is provided by a specific form of consequentialist ethics known as utilitarianism. Advanced by the nineteenth-century British philosophers Jeremy Bentham, James Mill, and Mill's son, John Stuart Mill, utilitarianism argues that morality has utility; it is useful to have morality in a society because that society will be more orderly, livable, and functional than a society with little morality. Since morality exists to make social life good, its purpose is human happiness. And human happiness is therefore the criterion of ethical action. In *Utilitarianism* (1863), John Stuart Mill writes that "the foundation of morals, Utility, or the Greatest Happiness Principle, holds that actions are right as they tend to promote happiness, wrong as they tend to produce the reverse of happiness" [1, p. 9].

Utilitarianism may sound simple, but it is ethically demanding. If I am considering a course of action, I can and should consider the happiness that it may bring me or that it may bring my family and me or that it may bring my friends and me. But utilitarianism requires that I weigh my happiness and the happiness of those I care about *equally* with the happiness of all people affected by the action. The happiness of all people involved counts equally, so the "Greatest Happiness Principle" means the greatest happiness for the greatest number of people and the least unhappiness for the fewest number.

It sounds as if utilitarianism asks us to somehow calculate, almost mathematically, the amount of happiness and unhappiness that will probably result from a given action. And in a way it does. Mill knew that there was no way to objectively measure happiness, but he argued that there are obvious conditions that tend to lead to happiness. When people have decent food and shelter, they are certainly more happy than when they don't. Physical or psychological pain obviously reduces happiness. People will generally let you know when they are unhappy and why. Basic common sense will let you arrive at a reasonable estimation of probable happiness and unhappiness.

Mill realized that not all human happiness is of the same quality. Some happiness is intense but short-lived and ultimately not that fulfilling. Watching Lindsey Vonn win the women's downhill at the Vancouver Winter Olympics may bring a period of very energetic happiness, but a week or month later that happiness is much less and probably gone entirely. Other forms of happiness are deeper, richer, and more enduring; the happiness felt by parents at the birth of a healthy child is not just intense but full and meaningful. So, Mill argued, as we mentally estimate the happiness that an action may produce, we have to take into account not just the *quantity* but also the *quality*. If an action results in a great quantity of low quality happiness, it may not be that moral.

The same holds true for unhappiness. My unhappiness at not being able to go skiing this weekend may be strong at the moment, but that unhappiness is fairly insignificant in the larger scheme. Unhappiness caused by, say, famine in Darfur may be less intense, but it may be more meaningful. So, in the utilitarian calculation, factor in both the *quality* and the *quantity* of unhappiness that will probably result.

Utilitarianism sounds good. It offers both a relatively straightforward way to arrive at ethical choices and a very rational way to justify those choices. But there are problems. Can we reliably predict the results our actions will have? Aren't there always unintended consequences? Can we really know what will lead to human happiness? After all, different things make different people happy, and what might make one person ecstatic could depress another person.

And there's a more serious problem. We hope that good actions have good results, but do good actions always have good results? And are there actions that might have, on the whole, good results, but that we'd still want to call bad? If I'm the accountant for a very wealthy client and have the opportunity to steal money from him, money that he will never know is missing and money that he has absolutely no need of, and if I give that money to charity, haven't I acted for the greatest happiness of the greatest number? Perhaps we shouldn't define morality by results.

2.   DEONTOLOGICAL ETHICS

The German philosopher Immanuel Kant rejected the view that good actions are defined by good results. Kant argued instead that consequences don't matter; the act itself is either right or wrong, no matter what happens afterward. *Deontos* is the Greek word for duty or obligation; Kant's ethics are deontological because they set out absolute duties that any moral agent must observe. There are moral principles or ethical rules that hold absolutely for all people in all times and all places. Following those principles means acting morally; violating them means acting immorally.

How do we know what those ethical duties are? Kant agrees with Mill on one point only: reason can determine ethical courses of action. Kant disagrees with Mill, however, on *how* reason works in ethics. For Kant, reason works in ethics this way. First, if you are faced with an ethical choice, ask yourself what general principle you would be following if you took a particular course of action. Second, ask yourself if you could rationally wish that everyone else followed that principle. (You universalize the principle.) If your answer is yes, the course of action is moral. If your answer is no, the course of action is immoral.

For example, if I am asked to alter the engineering report I've written and leave out relevant and pertinent information because the client doesn't want a federal agency to know, first I ask what general principle I would be following if I omitted that information from the report. The general principle would be something like "It's OK to submit incomplete reports" or, more generally, "It's OK to lie by omission." Second, I ask whether I could rationally wish that all people acted according to that principle. Could I reasonably want to live in a world where people acted on the rule that lying by omission was acceptable? What sort of world would that be? The answer, Kant believes, is obvious: I cannot rationally will that everyone live by that rule, and so the act of changing the report is wrong, and I have an absolute duty not to do so. Conversely, I can rationally wish that everyone followed the general principle that lying by omission is wrong, and therefore refusing to alter the report is morally right.

Deontological ethics holds that right action does not come from a calculation of consequences. If I act ethically, perhaps in a situation that requires me to make sacrifices, it is because of something much stronger than estimating results. I act rightly because I have an absolute obligation to do so. In a way, I have no choice. For Kant, ethics sets out categorical imperatives: moral principles are imperatives because you must follow them, no matter what the cost, and they are categorical because they hold in all circumstances and for all people.

In fact, Kant held that all moral principles can be reduced to a single categorical imperative. One version we've already covered: "Act only on the rule which you can at the same time will to become a universal law" [2, p. 971]. Kant offered an alternative version of the categorical imperative: "Act so that you treat humanity, whether yourself or someone else, never simply as a means, but always as an end" [2, p. 986]. Kantian ethics requires absolute respect for other persons as persons; the treatment you wish from others must be the treatment you give to others. This is the principle of universalization once again. Some have noted that Kant's statement of the categorical imperative bears a resemblance to ethical principles you may already know: "Therefore all things whatsoever ye would that men should do to you, do ye even so to them" (Matthew 7:12) or "And as ye would that men should do to you, do ye also to them likewise" (Luke 6:31).

But, as with utilitarianism, there are problems with deontological ethics. Is it reasonable to ignore results? If an action meets the test of universalizability but has disastrous consequences, is it really still moral? I might rationally wish that everyone in the world followed the principle "Lying is wrong" and not the principle "Lying is acceptable," but might there be situations in which telling the truth could lead to seriously hurt feelings, to economic losses, or—if I happen to be an employee of the CIA—to deaths? Most versions of deontology don't allow us to take into account the situation (e.g. "Lying is moral in situations where human lives are at risk"). But don't we need to take the situation into account? Utilitarianism lets us do that; deontology doesn't.

Further, let's be realistic. Faced with a moral decision, few people apply Kantian moral reasoning. And few people apply a utilitarian calculation of consequences. In all probability, people don't do either. Instead, they act out of habit. Good people—and there are good people— tend to act morally because it's in their nature to do so. And bad people— there are bad people—tend to act immorally because it's in their nature to do so. So, how is it that some people act rightly and others do not? Maybe we should focus, not on the results of the action, and not even on the action itself, but on the human being who is acting.

3.   VIRTUE ETHICS

Before utilitarianism and before deontological ethics, there was virtue ethics. Virtue ethics can be traced back to Confucius (6th century BCE), but for the Western tradition, it is Aristotle (4th century BCE) who provided the most influential formulation. While utilitarian and deontological ethics prevailed through the nineteenth and most of the twentieth century, virtue ethics, founded in ancient Greek philosophy, has made a remarkable comeback.

For virtue ethics, the question is not whether a particular course of action is right or wrong. The question is rather what sort of person tends to act rightly (or wrongly) and how that person got to be that way. What are the qualities that make a person we'd called a moral person? And how did that person acquire those qualities?

Aristotle held that there are two types of virtues. The first type, intellectual virtue, is composed of philosophical wisdom, *sophia,* and practical wisdom, *phronesis.* For Aristotle, habitual virtuous action depended on knowledge. The foolish and the inept could not act well. Graduates of CSM should have a surplus of *phronesis*; they know how to do things and get things done. If they have *sophia*, they know which things are worth doing and which are not.

In addition to the intellectual virtues—and equally important—are the eight moral virtues: prudence, justice, fortitude, courage, liberality, magnificence, magnanimity, and temperance. Each is a mean between two corresponding vices. If you fear to take any risk, you fail in courage, but if you repeatedly take foolhardy risks, you also fail. Real courage is the mean between extremes; a courageous person takes reasonable risks in situations that genuinely demand risk-taking and that offer significant results.

Similarly, virtuous people are generous (or "magnanimous") to others, but they take the middle path. They do not give away money to whomever asks without seeing whether there is real need and real benefit to be had. But neither do they refuse to give when they have the means to give and when others stand in genuine need of help.

In a sense, Aristotle holds that the virtuous person is *more* a human being than the non-virtuous person. Put simply, good people have realized their *telos*, the inherent principle of development within them, more fully and completely than bad people. Every being, in Aristotle's view, has an inherent goal toward which it aspires and grows. The *telos* of the acorn is to grow into a full, vital oak tree. The *telos* of a human is the complete development and expression of the essential capacities and talents inherent in him or her. The virtuous person has realized that *telos*; the unvirtuous person has failed to do so.

As with the acorn becoming an oak tree, virtues must grow. Habitual goodness does not happen automatically; it is the result of a growth that is identical with education (in the widest sense of the term). Good people learn goodness through their families, their schools and churches, their peers and elders, their culture as a whole. Once learned, right action becomes an integral part of character.

As with utilitarianism and deontology, there are problems with virtue ethics. How does an individual, even a habitually good individual, make a difficult decision in a morally complex situation? Utilitarianism and deontology give us rational methods for deciding complex ethical choices. The best that virtue ethics offers involves considering what a moral exemplar—a person whom you admire and would want to emulate—would probably do in that situation.

In addition, virtue ethics offers little hope for those whose life experiences have not yet given moral training and development. Both utilitarianism and deontology offer that person a rational means of making ethical decisions, no matter his or her inherent unethical tendencies. Virtue ethics can only suggest that the immoral or amoral person begin the process of ethical growth that his or her life has not included.

4.   ENVIRONMENTAL ETHICS

Environmental ethics investigates what, if any, moral obligations human have to the natural world and the rational grounds of those obligations. It asks what ethical principles should govern human behavior toward the environment. If we do have moral responsibilities, what are their objects? To whom or what do we have ethical obligations?

One general approach to environmental ethics holds that we do not have moral obligations to the natural world itself, but we do have obligations to other human beings who depend on the natural world and its resources for life. We have responsibilities to the natural world because it is necessary for human life and because harm to it can mean harm to other humans. This is **anthropocentric** ("human-centered) environmental ethics, and it claims that we have ethical obligations, not *directly to* the environment, but *in relation to* the environment as it affects human life. Some who hold anthropocentric ethics argue that, given how directly we depend on the natural world and given how complex and interwoven ecological systems are, we are obligated to take great care of the

...ent. They argue that damage to nature is, sooner or later, morally
eworthy damage to human life.

Some philosophers extend the anthropocentric environmental
ethics to **future generations**. They argue that it is not simply the present
generation that requires a healthy environment but generations to come as
well. This approach does not extend the moral community beyond human
beings; it simply includes people who are yet to be born but who may be
affected by our actions now. The argument is, very simply, that if our
actions cause irreparable environmental damage that degrades the lives of
future generations, those actions are wrong. This argument has particular
force in the case of non-renewable resources. Excessive use of a limited
resource, say petroleum, may deprive our children or grandchildren of that
which they need to lead good lives. In general, this view holds that we are
obligated to pass onto future generations a natural environment that is as
viable as the one we inherited—or better than the one we inherited—and
that we owe them sufficient resources to live lives as good as—or better
than—ours.

If we say that nature is important to us because it sustains our lives
and provides the raw material for civilization, we assign nature
instrumental value. An object has instrumental value if we use it to do
something. The instrumental value of a pen is that it allows us to write on
paper. The instrumental value of a plow is that it prepares a field for
sowing. The instrumental value of a tree is that it can be used for lumber,
for paper, or perhaps for shade on a hot day. The opposite of instrumental
value is **inherent** or **intrinsic** value. Objects with inherent value are
valuable in and of themselves, without regard to the uses to which they
might be put. For a collector of antique fountain pens, the pens collected no
longer have instrumental value and are rarely used for writing; they are
valued for themselves. An object with great inherent value, say a Van Gogh
painting, could be used instrumentally, say as a tray to serve drinks, but
that would be idiotic. Objects with extremely high inherent value tend to be
held in museums, libraries, and private collections, and, when they do come
on the market, they usually command astronomical prices.

Objects may have both instrumental and inherent value. A Rolex
watch keeps time, but it may actually not be as accurate as a much less
expensive Timex. The cheap watch has high instrumental and low inherent

value; the Rolex, for some people at least, has reasonably good instrumental but high inherent value. For some car enthusiasts, the '57 Chevy is reasonably instrumental since it still can get them from point A to point B pretty well, but its inherent value may be very high. And trees do provide lumber, paper, and shade, but if technological advances offered better ways of producing lumber, paper, and shade, would trees still have value? If your answer is no, trees have only instrumental value for you. If your answer is yes, the trees have some inherent value for you.

For some philosophers, our moral community ought to include more than just other human beings; it should include, in some fashion, the natural world in and for itself. This version of environmental ethics is called **nonanthropocentric** (or **biocentric**) because it suggests that our sense of moral value should no longer be focused only on humans but should include the larger natural world of which humans are a part. Nonanthropocentric ethics asks us to shift our ordinary moral perspective and see moral value, not just in people, but also in the larger community of living beings. In this view, environmental damage is wrong, not because it may hurt present or future generations, but because it is inherently wrong. Just as doing physical harm to another human being without overriding justification is wrong in anthropocentric ethics, so doing physical harm to the environment without overriding justification is wrong in nonanthropocentric ethics.

Most versions of nonanthropocentric ethics do not claim that nature (or parts of nature) has the same moral standing as people. Very few people would claim that our moral obligations to plants and animals are the same as our moral obligations to other humans. We make instrumental use of nature to survive, just as other animals do. Deontological ethics holds we should treat other people as ends in themselves and not as means to our ends, but it would be absurd to extend that view to include every living being on the earth. If someone eats a carrot for lunch, he or she is using the carrot as an instrument, as a means to an end, but under no ethical system is that an immoral action.

The issue, then, for nonanthropocentric ethics is exactly *how* the natural world should count in our moral considerations. There are some who, inspired by Western and Eastern religious traditions, seek to do harm to no living thing. For them, all life, no matter how apparently insignificant, is sacred and deserving of reverential care. The instrumental value of living beings matters little in comparison to their inherent value. All life is sacred, and all life requires moral consideration, almost the same moral consideration we grant to other people. In the view, we are not absolutely prohibited from cutting down a tree in order to make a house or taking antibiotics (literally, "against living things") to cure a disease, but we are obligated to consider every action that affects living beings carefully and responsibly.

One way to determine moral obligations to nature is to extend utilitarian ethics to include, not just the happiness and unhappiness of humans, but the happiness and unhappiness of all beings that can experience happiness and suffer unhappiness. And we may want to include them in the moral community in proportion to the degree that they can experience happiness and suffer unhappiness. Some animals—dolphins, elephants, chimpanzees—appear to be quite intelligent and able to experience pleasure and pain. We normally feel moral obligations to human infants but not to mature chimpanzees that are actually more intelligent and self-aware. What moral grounds do we have for treating the human babies with great care but locking chimpanzees in cages and using them for medical experimentation? The argument that our species just matters more than other species may be indefensible. If, according to utilitarianism, my happiness ought not to count more than the happiness of any other human being, so the happiness of my species (in getting to watch animals in zoos, in benefiting from medical advances) ought not to count more than the happiness of other species with the ability to experience happiness.

This argument, however, is not the same as the "reverence for all life" argument; it makes distinctions among the living beings to which we have moral obligations. A virus is arguably a living being, but its ability to experience happiness and unhappiness is probably non-existent. Taking antiviral medications for the sake of the health and happiness of the one who is infected is not only allowable but ethically mandated; however, causing the death of one who is capable of experiencing the fear of death for the sake of a passing moment of human happiness may not be ethical. Hunting elephants for ivory is now against the law in all countries. The trinkets and carvings made from ivory may bring some human pleasure, but the consensus today is that such happiness matters little in relation to the suffering caused to these remarkably sentient animals. And this view does not hold that we have obligations to animals equal to the obligations we have to other human humans; it says that we have obligations to them in proportion to their ability to experience the pleasures and pains we experience. In essence, this is the **animal rights** argument.

Another version of biocentric ethics focuses not on particular living beings but ⸴   ȝer ecological systems. As human moral beliefs developed, peoȷ ⁻   o live peacefully together in fairly stable communities. Simi˙   w, environmental ethics should make possible contin˖   le ecological communities that include people as well as animȧ   Traditional morality governs our interactions with other peoȴ   ȝociety; environmental morality should govern our interactionȿ   ˡogical communities we are a part of. One classic formulatioȵ ȼ   ⸴ ıs Aldo Leopold's "The Land Ethic" (1948). A farmer and fȯ ⸴ ⸴ter himself, Leopold saw how vast forests had been destroyed by unregulated logging, how overgrazing had ruined productive land, and how exploitative agriculture had damaged farmland. In response, Leopold argued the need for an "ecological conscience" or **land ethic**. For Leopold, the land meant not simply the soil itself but the entire system of life, from plants to insects to birds to mammals (including humans), that grows out of and depends on the earth. That living community, Leopold claims, is our moral community: "A thing is right when it tends to preserve the integrity, stability, and beauty of the biotic community. It is wrong when it tends otherwise" [3, p. 262].

Leopold's general principle seems clear enough, but how should it be applied? It may be easy to identify actions that harm the "integrity, stability, and beauty" of a biotic community on a large scale. In 1989, the supertanker *Exxon Valdez* hit a reef in Prince William Sound, Alaska, and spilled over ten million gallons of crude oil, devastating the ecology of the sound. For many people, the actions of the ship's captain, who may have been drunk at the time, were deeply immoral, not because of the loss of instrumentally valuable gasoline, but because of needless harm done to an inherently valuable ecosystem. Clearly, that would be a violation of the land ethic.

But what about harvesting trees for lumber? What about building a dam on a river for hydroelectric power and flood control? What about creating a new suburb on previously farmed land? Doesn't all human activity have an impact on some biotic community? Leopold acknowledges that humans must use natural resources, but he asks that we make moral distinctions between uses that permanently harm ecological systems and those that do not. Clear-cutting a forest may result in uncontrolled erosion that effectively destroys the local ecosystem, but selective logging in an overgrown forest may assure its health. Dams designed to allow fish to swim around them may do little harm to the river ecosystem. High-density housing developments might allow more land to be retained in a natural state.

Obviously, the land ethic requires careful judgment, but so do all traditional ethics. Leopold does not specify how large or small the biotic community must be to merit moral consideration. Damage to a major ecosystem such as Prince William Sound is certainly culpable, but is putting in a highway through a mountain valley or drilling for natural gas on the Western Slope of Colorado? Philosophers—and engineers—after Leopold have been working for answers to those sorts of questions.

One extension of the land ethic is **deep ecology.** In this view, human civilization is currently causing so much harm to the environment, which has morally inherent value and upon which human life depends, that dramatic changes are in order. Human populations should stabilize or decrease; natural resources should be extracted to meet basic human needs but little more; cultural values must shift from the acquisition of possessions to the living of spiritually enriching lives in close contact with nature. For deep ecologists, recognizing the moral standing of the environment requires fundamental changes in human culture and consciousness.

5.   ENGINEERING ETHICS

Engineering began in the military, and that heritage runs strong in the profession. Engineers see themselves as expert professionals, able to accomplish tasks assigned to them, responsible and loyal to their companies and clients. This history is evident even in titles: civil engineers were originally those who worked apart from the military (such as the Army Corps of Engineers) and who were therefore "civilian engineers."

In the nineteenth century, engineering became a distinct profession, with defined academic preparation and professional societies, such as the American Society of Civil Engineers (ASCE), the American Institute of Electrical Engineers (AIEE), the American Society of Mechanical Engineers (ASME), and the American Institute of Mining Engineers (AIME). The military tradition and the new professionalism came into conflict. ASCE and AIEE saw engineers as independent professionals whose expertise and special abilities granted them special standing and a degree of independence, while AIME and, to a degree, ASME conceived of engineers as technical employees whose obligations were entirely to the corporations employing them (7, p. 35). Neither view of engineering, however, emphasized moral behavior. Ethics was simply a personal concern, not a professional issue.

Toward the end of the nineteenth century and through the first part of the twentieth, a number of engineering disasters—mostly notably bridge failures—led to a dramatic change. In some cases, structural failures were the result of poor design and shoddy construction, and professional organizations strengthened their design and licensing requirements. In other cases, however, disaster resulted from overt unethical behavior on the part of engineers. In response, some engineering societies adopted formal codes of ethics: AIEE did so in 1912, ASCE and ASME in 1914, though AIME has never set forth a code of ethics (7, pp. 70, 84).

In the latter half of the twentieth century, engineering codes of ethics were revised and expanded. While each code has its specific provisions, the broad outlines of all codes are the same. The National Society of Professional Engineers, the most selective and prestigious engineering organization, sets out these "Fundamental Canons" of ethics:

Engineers, in the fulfillment of their professional duties shall:

1. Hold paramount the safety, health, and welfare of the public.

2. Perform services only in areas of their competence.

3. Issue public statements only in an objective and truthful manner.

4. Act for each employer or client as faithful agents or trustees.

5. Avoid deceptive acts.

6. Conduct themselves honorably, responsibly, ethically, and lawfully so as to enhance the honor, reputation, and usefulness of the profession. [4]

Note that Canon 4 continues the military heritage of engineering, while other canons speak to the engineering as an independent profession. Over the course of years, Canon 1, originally further down on the list, has risen to the top. For most engineers, this obligation overrides all other obligations and considerations. (The full NPSE Code of Ethics and codes from other organizations begin with basic principles or "canons" but then set out ethical obligations in great detail. You should read the complete NSPE code.)

Note also that Canon 1 agrees entirely with utilitarian ethics; most important in any moral choice is the "greatest happiness for the greatest number"—the public—no matter what the effect may be on the happiness of an individual engineer or his/her company. Canons 3 and 5 resonate with deontological ethics: telling the truth and avoiding lies are absolute obligations. Canon 6 echoes virtue theory; engineers should habitually practice the honorable behavior that makes them virtuous persons (and their profession as a whole worthy of respect).

The ASCE code is very similar, but Canon 1 has been expanded: "Engineers shall hold paramount the safety, health and welfare of the public and shall strive to comply with the principles of sustainable development in the performance of their professional duties," and "sustainable development" is defined as "the challenge of meeting human needs for natural resources, industrial products, energy, food, transportation, shelter, and effective waste management while conserving and protecting environmental quality and the natural resource base essential for future development" [5]. ASME has a similar provision, and IEEE requires its members to "to accept responsibility in making decisions consistent with the safety, health and welfare of the public, and to disclose promptly factors that might endanger the public or the environment" [6].

You may be surprised to see environmental issues mentioned in a code of professional ethics, but engineering organizations are in general agreement that our moral obligations do not begin and end with other human beings. There is some sense that engineers, whose work has massive impact on the environment, must take that impact into account. How far that obligation extends and exactly what it means are open to debate. Much of NHV is exactly about that debate.

References

[1]   J. S. Mill, *Utilitarianism*. Chicago: University of Chicago Press, 1906.

[2]   I. Kant, "Grounding for the metaphysics of morals." In Stephen M. Chan, ed. *Classics of Western Philosophy*, 6th ed., pp. 945-93. Indianapolis: Hackett, 2002,

[3]   A. Leopold, *A Sand County Almanac*. New York: Ballantine Books, 1966.

[4]   National Society of Professional Engineers, "NPSE code of ethics," http://www.nspe.org/Ethics/CodeofEthics/index.html Accessed Feb. 12. 2010.

[5]   American Society of Civil Engineers, "Code of ethics," http://www.asce.org/Content.aspx?id=7231 Accessed Feb. 12, 2010.

[6]   Institute of Electrical and Electronics Engineers, "IEEE code of ethics," http://www.ieee.org/portal/pages/iportals/aboutus/ethics/code.html Accessed Feb. 13, 2007.

[7]   E. T. Layton, *The Revolt of the Engineers: Social Responsibility and the American Engineering Profession*. Cleveland: Case Western Reserve, 1971.

Chapter 3. ENGINEERING AND WRITING

"Realize that [writing] is an important skill. It's critical to your success as an engineer. You can come up with the best design for some process, . . . but if you can't communicate that to people, it's not going to go anywhere."

-Amy Pruden, Engineering Research Center, Colorado State University [1]

Working engineers typically spend over a third of each day writing. And as engineers rise in the corporation or research center, that proportion only increases. There may be a technical writer on staff who can lend a hand, but the vast majority of writing is done by engineers themselves. The world is full of cases of technically competent engineers whose careers have stalled because they were unable to write effectively.

Engineers write memos, letters, proposals, executive summaries and abstracts, technical reports and special reports and standard reports, procedures, user handbooks, operation instructions, research studies, patents—the list goes on and on. The amount of paper generated in a complex design process may actually outweigh the result of that process, even if the result is a very large bit of machinery.

As an engineer, you will not just be writing to and for other engineers. Engineering companies are increasingly being held accountable for their decisions, and those decisions must be clearly and persuasively explained to clients, to government agencies, to the public at large. Successful engineers are able to write not just a variety of different kinds of writing, but for a variety of readers and audiences.

In "How Should Engineers Write? What Their Managers Say," Kathleen Mohn describes four problems that engineers encounter as they write. First, many engineers tend to believe that facts speak for themselves and that data alone suffices. In reports, they tend to describe the procedure used to arrive at the data and then dump in the data, sometimes pages and pages of it. Sheer data, however, means little. It has to be interpreted, and that interpretation takes place in writing. The engineer who authors the report may clearly understand what the data mean and what their implications are, but unless meaning and implications are clearly communicated, the report serves no useful purpose [2, p. 1].

Second, some engineers, while careful and precise with data, tend to be careless and imprecise with sentences. They tend to believe writing is good enough if someone else, with generally the same background, can make out the meaning. While writing style has moved in the direction of conversational English, engineering writing should still be professional— clear, direct, and accurate. It should avoid slang and "Shop Talk," and, at the same time, avoid extreme formality. In writing, the goal is to communicate effectively and economically with readers. Correct grammar and logical phrasing do that.

The third problem managers saw was overreliance on technical jargon. Yes, engineers need to sound professional and demonstrate expertise, but too much jargon obscures rather than communicates [2, p. 5]. Long phrases laden with nominalizations (verbs converted into nouns by adding –tion or –tivity) may sound impressive, but, as Mohn notes, "three-dimensional rectilinear productivity habitat" has only the vaguest meaning, and once the reader realizes the phrase really means "cubicle," the laugh is on the writer.

Finally, whether in short email messages and memos or in substantial reports, many engineers failed to organize the material clearly and logically. Significant facts and conclusions get lost in the mass of data. The big picture gets lost in a welter of details, and important points hide in a thicket of relatively unimportant points. Document organization is not that different from good design [2, p. 6].

NHV is not a course in technical communication, but the basic principles you learn and practice—precise and economical statement, conversational yet professional style, logical organization—carry over directly into professional writing.

References

[1] Writing @ CSU, "Engineers on Writing,"
http://writing.colostate.edu/collections/engineering/writers.cfm
Accessed Mar. 15, 2010.

[2] Kathleen Mohn, "How Should Engineers Write? What Their
Managers Say," *Newsletter*, IEEE Professional Communication
Society, March/April 2002,
http://ewh.ieee.org/soc/pcs/newsletter/archive/pdfs/mar_apr0
2.pdf Accessed Mar. 5, 2010.

Chapter 4. CRITICAL READING

Your reading education probably began with learning the alphabet and sounds. Once you started recognizing the symbols and associating them with the proper sounds, you had "learned to read." Thereafter, as your vocabulary increased, you were expected to be able to read anything thrown at you. There's a flaw with this concept, though. You encounter a vast variety of texts and read them for very different purposes, so you shouldn't expect to read them all the same way. This chapter seeks to provide you with some tips and tools to make you a more active, successful reader of varied texts.

You may have found that there are types of reading you are better at than others. Perhaps you comprehend 140-character bits better than lengthy articles. Maybe you love reading novels, but get lost in non-fiction. Perhaps you've been turned off reading altogether by literary analysis or confusing materials in a previous class. Whatever the case, the following sections can help make you a faster, better reader in all contexts.

The first section covers **active reading and reading strategies**. Section 2 provides tips on understanding **structure and main ideas**. Section 3 outlines key concepts in locating **arguments and evidence**. Finally, the fourth section discusses ways to **write about and discuss** the reading you do.

1.   ACTIVE READING STRATEGIES

GET TO KNOW YOURSELF AS A READER

An important first step in becoming an active reader is to understand your personal preferences and skills in reading. Experiment to find the conditions and practices that most help you. Answer the following questions to get started:

- What times of day work best for you to read? When can you best focus?

- What level of distraction (noise, movement, other people) can you handle and still comprehend a text? Under what circumstances can you best focus?

- What is the time threshold for your concentration? Can you read for 2 hours straight or for fifteen-minute intervals with short breaks?

- Are there breaks in your schedule when you can plan to read at a certain time every day or every week?

- What reading assignments are easiest for you to comprehend and retain long-term? What types of readings are most difficult to understand and remember?

- Have you used any techniques like previewing, skimming, scanning, and note-taking that enhance your ability to read effectively?

BECOMING AN ACTIVE READER

Passive reading is the plodding, word-by-word reading that often results in getting to the bottom of the page and realizing that you haven't comprehended anything. **Active reading**, by contrast, is a process of engaging with the text and making choices about how you read based on what you need to do with the information.

An important part of being an active reader is knowing that you'll approach different materials in different ways. You'll vary the level of focus and length of time you spend reading different types of text. You can kick back a bit when scanning internet news, but have to buckle down to study a chemistry chapter or analyze an argument.

To help you focus on harder material and increase your speed in getting through it, try **eye-hand tracking techniques**. There are lots of ways to do this, all of which involve keeping your eyes focused on the text and moving down the page at a steady, but variable, speed. You can really increase your reading speed with practice of these techniques, and you will benefit from having a strategy that can be adjusted for any reading. Try each of these techniques to see what works best for you:

Use a straight edge or piece of paper to draw down the page as you read, line by line. Keep the card moving at a constant pace to encourage your eyes to read smoothly and more quickly.

With three or four fingers (probably of your dominant hand), curl them into a comfortable position that forms a flat underlining surface. Place your fingers under the line of text and glide along the line. When you get to the end, slide your fingers back quickly to the beginning of the next line and repeat. Get into a comfortable rhythm, slowing down when the text is difficult and speeding up when you want to increase your speed.

Use a finger to run down the margin of the text, setting a pace for reading the lines. This technique can work best when rereading or reading easier material.

For quicker skimming and scanning, especially when looking for a particular word, fact, or idea, use your finger to trace a zig-zag pattern through the text.

Practice seeing more than one word at a time, a technique called "chunking." You don't have to focus individually on each word and hear it in your head; rather, your eyes can be trained to see a chunk of words and comprehend them faster than word-by-word reading.

How you read a text (and choose to use the eye-hand tracking techniques) will vary based on *why* you'll read a given text. Therefore, one of the most crucial choices an active reader makes depends on the **reader's purpose**. Consider first what you'll need to do with the text:

- Will you need to regurgitate facts for a test?
- Are you being asked to write about the ideas?
- Are you comparing this reading with another?
- Will you be expected to discuss the text?
- Are you looking for main ideas or details and evidence?
- How does this reading relate to other things you've read?
- How does the text fit into the course or assignment?

- Will you need to take formal notes or annotate?

These questions can help you determine whether you can get by with surface reading or if you need to focus on deep reading. **Surface reading** is reading at a basic, literal level. You accept what is there as fact, and can sometimes gloss over things superficially. You can probably remember the information for an exam, but don't benefit from any long-term retention. By contrast, **deep reading** or **close reading** involves analysis, synthesis, and problem solving. You consider the structure and meaning of arguments, make connections to other subjects and texts, and question and respond to the author's ideas. You seek to apply information in new contexts and add your voice to the academic conversation.

2.   GETTING STARTED—DEEP READING

PREVIEW

Begin by looking at the text's title, author, and other preliminary information. Read the opening and closing paragraphs of the piece, an abstract or summary if it has one, and any publication information you have available.

Start with thinking through **what you know** about the text. Take a look at the title and abstract, then Google unfamiliar concepts if you need to.

- What do you know about this topic?
- What do you know about the general debate (or consensus) on this topic?
- Where does your knowledge come from?
- What is your opinion?

Consider the **rhetorical context**. All writing is done by a real person for a specific purpose. It's important to know why this piece of writing was created. Look at the author's bio and bibliographic information and try to answer the following:

- Who wrote it and what is the author's background and expertise?

- For what audience was it written? For what purpose?

- Where and when was it published?

Having a sense of what you know and the rhetorical context will help you determine the relevance of the reading to your task, the reliability of the source, and how to approach the reading assignment. You'll be better prepared to use your active reading strategies to get the most out of your time reading.

ACTIVE READING

Active reading comes from engagement with the text, so as you begin to read an assignment, make sure to have a pen or pencil in hand. Highlighting is valuable for some purposes, but isn't as interactive as annotation. **Annotation** is critically examining and explaining your thoughts on a text as you take notes. There are many ways to annotate a text, and you should find what works best for you. Imagine you are talking to the writer as you jot down questions and comments in the margins. In particular, the more you can **put the ideas in your own words**, the more clearly you will understand the essay. The act of paraphrasing and questioning helps make the text your own and assures you'll remember the ideas for much longer than if you just passively read.

Following is a list of techniques you can choose from in developing the strategies that are most valuable for you:

- Find the thesis and other claims. Paraphrase them in the margins.

- Identify the author's assumptions.

- Comment on evidence used as support for claims. Is it reasonable? Is it specific?

- Identify key terms and definitions.

- Note your agreement on specific arguments.

- Note any contradictions within the reading or with your own understanding.

- Play devil's advocate.

- Identify values expressed in the author's writing.

- Question the writer.

- Make connections to other readings or lectures.

- Consider what the author is omitting or oversimplifying.

- Mark clues to the author's purpose and audience for this argument.

- Note indications of the author's bias, values, or ethical principles.

- Indicate your personal response to the ideas.

- Use different colors to code themes and connections.

To give you an idea of what good annotation looks like, read the following paragraph from Garrett Hardin's "The Tragedy of the Commons" and note the types of annotations you see. Consider how your annotations may be different from this example:

That morality is system-sensitive escaped the attention of most codifiers of ethics in the past. "Thou shalt not..." is the form of traditional ethical directives which make no allowance for particular circumstances. The laws of our society follow the pattern of ancient ethics, and therefore are poorly suited to governing a complex, crowded, changeable world. Our epicyclic solution is to augment statutory law with administrative law. Since it is practically impossible to spell out all the conditions under which it is safe to burn trash in the back yard or to run an automobile without smog control, by law we delegate the details to bureaus. The result is administrative law, which is rightly feared for an ancient reason -- *Quis custodies ipsos custodes?* --Who shall watch the watchers themselves? John Adams said that we must have a "government of laws and not men." Bureau administrators, trying to evaluate the morality of acts in the total system, are singularly liable to corruption, producing a government by men, not laws. [1, p. 308]

Who are these?
Biblical reference here

Look up this word

Statutory law=passed by a legislature? Admin. law=set by an agency?

Does Hardin think all admin. law is bad? Just some? Can we live without it?

It's true that you are very busy as a student at the Colorado School of Mines, and sometimes "overwhelmed" or "slammed" may better describe your schedule. You'll want to get the most out of the reading you do so that you're not wasting time. Most often, reading an assignment once will suffice and your instructors will be pleased.

However, for some reading assignments, especially those about which you will write or present, go through the reading a couple different times. Each time, you can focus on new elements of the essay and gain deeper understanding. For example, the first time reading, you may want to go quickly to ascertain the main points. Then, for a second pass at the reading, focus on good annotation, defining terms you don't understand, questioning the author's ideas, and making personal comments. Finally, read the piece a third time to determine the structure of the argument and the connections between sections. You can sketch an outline of the article and add notes about the purpose for each section.

Another technique is to first read literally, seeking to comprehend and apply what you've read. Then read a second time to analyze: synthesize the piece with others you've read and evaluate the validity of the ideas.

REVIEW

To make sure that all the time you just spent reading an essay is not wasted, take time to review and reflect on what you've read. Often, this is as simple as considering what you thought about the reading. It's a great idea to write down this reflection in your notebook or on the essay itself. If you've made some good annotations on the text, you probably have some unanswered questions or undefined terms to research further. Spend a few minutes investigating these loose ends right away so you can apply the ideas to your mental conception of the essay. Other ways to review and reflect are these:

- Talk about the issues with classmates, friends, or family.
- Paraphrase main ideas.
- Map out the ideas from the reading in a graphic organizer.
- Outline your position on the issue.
- Write a response paragraph to the author.
- Search the web for related stories and arguments.
- Ask questions about the essay.

Having a written record of your thoughts and reactions will help you prepare for discussion and exams, and will assure that you can accurately represent the reading assignment in your written work. Again, the more you can process the ideas of the reading in your own words, the more likely you are to internalize the ideas for the long term.

3.   IDENTIFYING STRUCTURE OF A READING

CLAIMS AND EVIDENCE IN YOUR READING

The argument chapter of this text explains some of the key terms important to this section on reading. We'll work through some examples of claims and evidence in example paragraphs to help illustrate the key points you're looking for when reading an essay.

Sometimes a reading will have a very straightforward structure that will mirror the way you were probably taught to write: thesis, followed by (usually 3 or 4 points of) support—or in other terms, claim, followed by evidence. This structure can really help you as a reader to determine the main claims and the evidence that supports them. Following is an example from Elizabeth Gee's essay "Moral Vision and the Landscape of Engineering Professionalism."

The development of professional codes of ethics is often discussed in response to issues of professional integrity. (1) Clearly there are ways in which these standards contribute to the professional's ethical integrity. (2) They bring focus and force to ethical predicaments that otherwise might go unattended. (3) Codes of ethics provide a means of participating in the moral life of the professional community and sharing in the professional consensus concerning courtesy, responsibility, and competency. (4) They relieve some of the extraordinary psychological burden and moral aggravation that professionals otherwise would face. (5) And, to an important degree, these standards distinguish the professional's obligations that are role specific from those of ordinary persons. [2]

(1) CLAIM
(2) EVIDENCE

(3) EVIDENCE

(4) EVIDENCE

(5) EVIDENCE

In the paragraph above, Gee is claiming that codes of ethics are beneficial to professionals in several ways. Then she outlines the reasons or evidence for this claim by listing several positive aspects of codes of ethics in the rest of the paragraph.

In other cases, you won't be so lucky as to have the claim first and evidence immediately following. You may have to work a little harder to determine the function of a particular sentence or to elucidate the connections between ideas in a paragraph. In the following example, a paragraph is examined to determine claims and evidence. Note that annotation can play a key role in a reader's ability to see what it happening in a section. This section comes from Karen Chapman's argument in *Taking Sides* called "Brave Nuclear World?"

(1) In September 2005, a report on the health impacts of Chornobyl by the UN Chernobyl Forum (seven UN agencies plus the World Bank and officials from Belarus, Ukraine, and Russia) said only 50 deaths could be attributed to Chornobyl and ultimately 4,000 will die as a result of the accident. (2) The Chernobyl Forum report acknowledges that nine children died from thyroid cancer and that 4,000 children contracted the disease, but puts the survival rate at 99 percent. (3) It denies any link with fertility problems and says that the most significant health problems are due to poverty, lifestyle (e.g., smoking, poor diet), and emotional problems, especially among evacuees. (4) Marples notes that the overall assessment of the Chernobyl Forum is "a reassuring message."[3]

(1) EVIDENCE

(2) EVIDENCE

(3) EVIDENCE

(4) CLAIM

In this example, the paragraph begins with several points of evidence from the Chernobyl Forum and the claim comes at the end of the paragraph. This section may imply that the author Chapman agrees that Chernobyl didn't have any terrible health effects; however, her argument is much to the contrary. We find that Charman is offering this evidence in order to refute it. Her next paragraph begins with the following sentence: "The reality on the ground offers a different picture...the incidence of thyroid cancer is 10,000 times higher than before the accident." If you are reading carefully, you will pick up on these nuances in content and be able to understand the structure and purpose of the reading.

BASIC TYPES OF ORGANIZATIONAL STRUCTURE

To best understand your reading assignments, it helps to know something about their structure and the purposes for different sections. In the basic sense, you'll be looking to find the elements of a good argument, such as thesis statement, claims, reasons, evidence, and refutations of opposing viewpoints. However, you also want to think about how the piece was constructed and why the author chose to organize it in such a way.

Most argumentative writing is organized in a **logical** way, meaning it moves from general to specific ideas, from the cause of a problem to its effects, or from a controversy to a solution. As a reader of this type of writing, you want to be on the lookout for gaps in the logic, poor evidence, and unsubstantiated claims.

Some writing uses **chronology** to present ideas, possibly moving from the past to the present, or from the present to the future, asking the reader to follow a timeline. Other times, a writer will use **spatial** organization to construct the essay. This is most often used when describing a physical space or set of characteristics. If a writer chooses a chronological or spatial organizational pattern, consider how focusing on time progression or visual layout is helpful to you as a reader seeking to understand the topic.

THE STRUCTURE AND PURPOSE OF PARAGRAPHS OR SECTIONS

When you look at a paragraph or section of a reading, in addition to determining claims and evidence, you should also think about what purpose the paragraph or section serves in the essay. This can help you understand the overall structure and purpose of the reading as a whole. The writer has designed the reading to provide a particular progression of ideas, and thinking about the following purposes will help you decode the reading.

- Background: historical perspective or important background information

- Definition: terms and concepts defined for the reader
- Narration: tells a story or gives an anecdote
- Description: gives details on what is seen, heard, smelled, felt, or tasted
- Process: explains the steps or sequence of a process
- Analogy: draws a comparison between two topics or examples
- Classification: groups concepts or events into categories
- Comparison: shows the similarities and differences between topics
- Cause/Effect: highlights the influence of one event on another or explains why something happened
- Developing a reason: elaborates on reasons or evidence for a claim
- Opposing Views: presents arguments that counter the author's thesis
- Refutation: show weaknesses in opposing views

You may find it helpful to number the paragraphs of a reading and label the sections by purpose in the margin. This way you can get a sense of the progression of the reading. You'll also be able to easily identify the most crucial sections or techniques the writer has used. Knowing the purpose of a section can also help you in your discussions and written work on a reading.

4.   TECHNIQUES FOR UNDERSTANDING STRUCTURE

Instructors will often ask you to take notes on your reading, and even if they don't require notes, you should get in the habit of keeping a notebook on paper or in a digital file. Notes are permanent records of what you thought as you read the work, and are helpful for writing assignments, discussion, and exams on material. You can use several methods for note-taking on a reading and the following examples will illustrate some of the most popular or effective techniques. Try these out to see what method makes the most sense for you. Different classes, texts, and assignments may require different types of notes.

For each type of note-taking described below, there is a short example of the technique based on James Rachels' chapter "What is Morality?" from his book *The Elements of Moral Philosophy*.

BEFORE-DURING-AFTER GRID

This method works with the concept of previewing, reading, and reviewing mentioned earlier in the section. Divide your paper into three columns. In the first column, jot down questions and comments you have based on your preview of the text. As you read, make notes in the middle column, trying to catch main points and examples. You can also comment on and question the ideas here. Finally, use the third column to reflect on the information you just read and draw conclusions. Here's an example:

BEFORE	DURING	AFTER
He says he will define morality, but is that possible?	Rachels uses examples of injured or sick children	It is hard not to have an opinion on the cases he presents, but I'm not sure I see his argument on what's right for each one
Rachels is a philospher	He gives arguments from all the people involved in the case	
Morality is the same as religion, isn't it?	He seems to give a decision on what is morally right at the end	He argues that we need to eliminate feelings in morality, but I think emotion is very important in these situations. If we didn't have emotion, we wouldn't care what
I think that morality is different for every person	Definitions on reason and impartiality	
From the section titles, it seems like the	Seems to be against	

he will try to describe moral actions with some examples	emotion and feelings "Minimum conception of morality"	happened to anyone This sounds good on the surface, but how can we convince people to use this process?

QUESTIONS—OBSERVATIONS—EVIDENCE

For this technique, you'll use a similar three-column format, but slightly vary the content from the previous example. This time, you identify key questions in the first column (questions can be added at any time during the reading process). In the second column, record what you notice about how the text is written and try to answer the questions you have in column one. In the third column, make note of the reasons, examples, and evidence you find in the reading. Here's an example of this form of note-taking:

QUESTIONS	OBSERVATIONS	EVIDENCE
Who is James Rachels?	He is a philosopher at Univ. of Alabama	He is very methodical in his analysis
How are the cases chosen?	He seems to have picked all child illness cases	These cases all pull on the emotions and reactions of the reader
How are the cases analyzed?	He presents arguments of each party involved in the case	He evaluates the most moral choice for each case after considering sides
Why are three example cases presented?	It seems that each case gets progressively complicated	The cases help him define the complexity of morality in the end

CONCEPTUAL NOTES

In this style of note-taking, the focus is on finding the major features of the reading. Take notes on what you already know about the topic and author before you read. As you read, look for the thesis, evidence, key terms, analogies, assumptions, contradictions in terms, opposing views, and your personal response. It's best to start with all these categories listed on your sheet and try to fill in each category as you read. A shortened example of this technique is below for Rachels' chapter:

> WHAT I KNOW: Morality is the difference between right and wrong and is usually based on personal values.
>
> RHETORICAL CONTEXT: Rachels has a PhD in philosophy and this is a textbook for Students. It should be written at an introductory level.
>
> MAIN IDEA/THESIS: Rachels wants to define the idea of morality in a broad way
>
> KEY TERMS: "minimum conception of morality," reason, impartiality
>
> ASSUMPTIONS: He assumes the reader will have an emotional response to the cases
>
> OPPOSING VIEWS: he presents the views of each side of the argument, but critiques some more than others based on his definition of morality
>
> PERSONAL RESPONSE: I think the definition of morality can be applied universally, but that people are often too involved emotionally in their own situations to be able to make the reasonable choice.

LINEAR NOTES

In this technique, you seek to follow the reading chronologically and identify key points and the purpose of sections as you go. This type is easiest when the reading has distinct headings. If the writer doesn't provide headings, you'll need to carefully notice any shifts in purpose and meaning between paragraphs. Here is an example:

Section 1: Rachels says morality is hard to define, but he's going to try.

Section 2: Baby Theresa case. This brings up thequestion of who benefits from Theresa's life, the idea that we shouldn't use people for our own benefit, and that killing is wrong no matter what

Section 3: Jodie and Mary. These conjoined twins illustrate the arguments that life is sacred and that we should save one if we can. Parents wanted to let them live naturally for religious reasons— reader starts to questions who can or should decide what happens in life or death situations.

Section 4: Tracy Latimer's "mercy killing". Here we see that there can be a slippery slope in moral arguments and that it is wrong to punish the handicapped

Section 5: Reason and Impartiality are defined and their relationship to morality is made clear. Emotions can cloud judgment and all people should be considered equally.

Section 6: To be moral, we should consider all parties involved and try to make the choice that has the best reasons behind it.

OTHER OPTIONS FOR NOTES

These examples are just a few of the possibilities for note-taking. You can also use outlining, clustering or webs, the Toulmin method, the Cornell method, and more. It's most important to find a method that makes sense to you and that you can easily read and reference when you need to.

5.   READING FOR WRITING AND DISCUSSION

In Nature and Human Values your reading assignments are often the basis for class discussions and presentations and your writing assignments. It's crucial that you have a sense of the writer's main argument and that you've considered your reaction as well. In addition, you want to make sure you have worked through the difficult passages in the text, which may take some extra thought or internet searching.

Consider that writers may come from a different time or culture, so you may have to work to bridge that gap in context for the ideas. As mentioned in the claims and evidence examples, the writer may express values that contradict their own in order to make a point. Make sure you don't misunderstand these arguments for the writer's ideas. Writers often tend to reference outside examples of events in the news, works of art, historical figures, etc., which you may not understand. Look these up so you have a more complete understanding of the author's intent. The same goes for unfamiliar vocabulary. Some words aren't crucial to the text, but other unfamiliar terms will be key to getting the writer's argument. Use the numerous quick tools at your disposal and look them up.

As you prepare for a discussion or writing assignment on a reading, consider doing the following:

- Review your reading notes.
- Prepare questions for instructor or class.
- Answer the questions yourself.
- Identify important quotations.
- Paraphrase sections to make sure you understand.
- Reread for clarity.
- Identify connections to lectures or previous knowledge.
- Research online to find connections.
- Discover what faculty at Mines are researching.

References

[1] G. Hardin, "The Tragedy of the Commons." In *Environmental Ethics: Readings in Theory and Application.* 2nd ed. L.P. Pojman, Ed. New York: Wadsworth , 1998, pp. 305-312.

[2] E. Gee. "Moral Vision and the Landscape of Engineering Professionalism." National Society of Professional Engineers, Ethics Resources. [Online] Available: http://www.nspe.org/Ethics/. Accessed March 17, 2010.

[3] K. Chapman. "Brave Nuclear World?" from *Taking Sides: Clashing Views in Science Technology and Society*. T. Easton, ed. Boston: McGraw-Hill, 2007, pp. 104-113.

Chapter 5. WRITING

1.   PRE-WRITING

CHOOSING A TOPIC

A first step in writing a paper is choosing a topic you are interested in and even care for. Almost any subject is multifaceted, so if you are engaged in researching and writing about it, you might discover its sides and intricacies more easily.

Writers tend to choose broad topics first and then narrow them down later to make them fit the length and scope of the paper they write. If you are working on a five-page essay, a topic such as engineering and ethics is too broad; entire books have been written on this subject and you cannot possibly cover all the moral aspects of the engineering profession in five pages. You could discuss, for instance, how "safety," a number one priority in the codes of ethics for engineers today, has replaced the issue of "loyalty to one's company."

PRE-WRITING

After you chose a topic, you should start generating ideas about this topic. Techniques such as brainstorming, freewriting, clustering, and questioning can help writers get ideas, see connections among various notions and concepts, research the topic, and organize the essay.

Brainstorming requires writers to generate a variety of ideas about a topic rapidly. The process of creating lists of points, questions, answers, and notes may lead to ideas that writers want to pursue in their essays. Full sentences that are grammatically correct should not interest writers who brainstorm because they are trying to generate many ideas

44

quickly. The longer the lists of words and phrases, the better the writers' chances of finding interesting viewpoints. Consider the following example of brainstorming "engineering and ethics."

Concern about the safety of the public

Loyalty to the company

Honesty, integrity

Loyalty to science

Designing safer and more efficient products

Present objective data

Respect different colleagues and their ideas

Similar to brainstorming, **freewriting** focuses more on the subject at hand. Based on the idea that writing is a process, freewriting asks you to write constantly for a period of time. Try to write as much as possible without thinking about the result, grammar, spelling, or editing. Without letting your hand stop, write down every idea and sentence that pops into your head and do not think of their relevance and depth. Read what you wrote and repeat this exercise after 10 minutes. Then, arrange your ideas in the proper order and decide on the ideas that you will use in your paper. Below is an an example of freewriting on the broad topic of genetic engineering in *Oryx and Crake* by Margaret Atwood.

Crake and the other scientists create new species such as rakunks, pigoons, and wolvogs. Using advanced techniques in genetic engineering, Crake also creates a new species of people called the Crakers. The Crakers and Children of Crake seem to be perfect because of their physical beauty and their lives that resemble the existence of animals; their impact on the environment is minimal since they eat only grass. However they lack social skills, have no sense of history and individuality, and they were taught to disregard religion, art, and leadership. Atwood shows that science and genetic engineering, if not regulated, ultimately lead to the downfall of humankind. Crake attempts to control human reproduction with a pill, destroy humanity, and replace humans with new species that are genetically engineered.

A number of different subtopics emerge: genetic engineering and regulations; genetic engineering and eugenics; perfection of a whole species versus the quest for individuality and originality; genetic engineering and the environment. Choose one of these subtopics and try to freewrite again.

Clustering or **mapping** is a visual way of discovering ideas and relationships among them. Take a sheet of paper and write your topic in the middle; then circle words connected to your topic and begin to make clusters around them. Note which ideas are connected and decide how you will use them in your paper.

Questioning is another way to discover ideas about a topic. Write down any questions you can think of about a specific topic and use the answers to your questions as ideas you can develop in your essays. Imagine that you are discussing the topic with one of your professors or with an expert in the field. What questions would you ask him or her? More often than not, the answer(s) to specific questions can become ideas for your argument or your body-paragraphs. The following example considers several questions about the *Challenger* disaster.

- Did Roger Boisjoly do everything he could to prevent the disaster? What did he do? What could he have done?

- Do you think the outcome would have been different had Boisjoly alerted the press and the crew members? How?

- What does Boisjoly teach us about truth, integrity, honesty, and ethics?

- What are Boisjoly's values and how far is he willing to go to defend his values?

- What advice does he give students at the end of his speech?

- Why should engineers study ethics?

2.   WRITING A FIRST DRAFT

CONSTRUCTING A THESIS STATEMENT

Simply put, the thesis statement constitutes the main point of the essay. It is expressed in a sentence or two at the end of the introduction and it guides readers toward the main ideas in the essay. Best thesis statements are clear, original, debatable, and focused. It is acceptable to write a thesis statement when you start writing the essay or after you have finished the essay. Some writers prefer to write their introductions and thesis statements after they complete the whole essay because they feel they have a better idea of what their essays are about. Decide what works best for you, but remember that your thesis statement is one of the most important sentences of your essay and the one which needs the most revision and rethinking. Thus, you should revise your thesis statement several times before you turn in the paper.

Here are some examples of thesis statements. Make sure to differentiate between weak thesis statements and strong and original ones.

I think it is important to have a code of ethics. (This thesis is only an opinion not backed by reasoning; it is too general, weak, and ordinary).

The Challenger exploded because of faulty O-rings. (This thesis states a fact and does not develop any idea or provide any details about this fact).

Living in an apartment has many advantages. (It is vague, general and not debatable enough).

This essay will discuss genetic engineering or *In this paper, I will discuss genetic engineering.* (Avoid announcing the main point of your essay or reminding readers that you are writing an essay. State your main point about genetic engineering directly).

Roger Boisjoly was right because he stood up for what he believed in. (This thesis remains vague, opinionated, and unoriginal).

Reading texts and writing essays develop skills and qualities that can make one successful in life because they demand critical thinking, attention to details, originality, and effective communication. (This thesis is better because it is debatable; it does not state the obvious; and it reveals what the essay will discuss).

Criteria for a Good Thesis Statement/Argument

- A good thesis statement is argumentative – something requiring proof before we believe it.

- A good argument presents an interesting and original idea and the reasoning behind this idea. This idea is not a summary or report of what you have read, but your own insightful position.

- Best arguments answer questions such as "why?", "so what?" and are debatable. The answer to the "why?" question will offer insight into your reasoning behind your main idea. The answer to the "so what?" question will explain the significance of your argument.

- The thesis statement provides direction for the essay. This works with laying out what the essay will prove.

- It is not a "duh" statement, such as *Racism is bad.* Good thesis statements usually say something a little strange rather than what is expected.

- It is narrow and specific. This means it may only apply to the issues or the texts you are analyzing.

- It is not a universal truth-type of sentence; you do not have to prove that the earth is round; you need to focus only on the issues you address in the paper or the texts you are analyzing and formulate a thesis statement about them.

- It should use specific words to explain rather than fuzzy ones such as *interesting, good, bad, different,* and *similar.* These words are fuzzy because they are hard to quantify and define.

SUPPORTING YOUR THESIS WITH EVIDENCE

Once you have written a working thesis statement, the next step is to support it with evidence, with reasons that will convince readers of the validity of your thesis. Without good evidence, you cannot persuade your readers of anything. The evidence, which will be organized into the essay's body-paragraphs, refers to information that justifies your thesis, clarifies it, and explains it. There are several types of evidence, including definitions, facts, examples, statistics, critical analysis, speculation, quotations from primary and outside sources, and personal experience. It is important that your evidence is solid and reliable; in other words, your evidence should be relevant, detailed, and accurate.

- Definitions of concepts and phrases will explain their meaning and make your ideas more credible.

- Facts are indisputable and thus believable because anyone researching a subject would produce the same information.

- Examples are defined as problems used to illustrate a concept and are meant to put abstract ideas in a more specific context.

- Statistics are data translated into numbers, charts, and figures and are meant to support a claim rapidly.

- Critical analysis refers to inquisitive and stimulating details about texts that both inform readers and make them view texts in new ways.

- Speculation could be used in essays when it is supported by facts. With speculation, writers try to open up new areas of inquiry that may produce new knowledge.

- Quotations from primary sources are crucial to support your ideas no matter how original and insightful these ideas are. Through quotations, you show that your claims are justified. Quotations and paraphrase from outside sources are equally important.

- Personal experience and observation can be useful when we feel we have gained enough knowledge about a subject or issue. Remember that our personal experience may not be totally reliable.

DEVELOPING PARAGRAPHS

Paragraphs explain in detail the main points of your argument. Your ideas could be insightful and smart, but if you cannot present them in a coherent fashion, they lose their charm altogether. Your readers will be confused if they read a paragraph about ten different ideas written in ten sentences that have nothing to do with one another. Paragraphs are all about packaging ideas and combing facts, analysis, examples, and quotations in a way that makes sense and contributes to your overall argument. Your thoughts and evidence should follow one another logically and create a paragraph that flows well.

Good paragraphs have a clear purpose and a sense of direction and unity. To preserve this unity, paragraphs are organized around one main idea and make one point; anything that does not support that point should be deleted from the paragraph because it does not belong there. For the sake of clarity, coherence, and unity, paragraphs need topic sentences that can help both writers and readers explain what the main point of a paragraph is. A topic sentence is a sentence that explains the main idea of a paragraph and controls the rest of the paragraph. The body of a paragraph explains, develops, and supports with evidence the topic sentence's main claim. The topic sentence is usually the first sentence of a paragraph, but it may also come after a transition sentence.

Keys to Forming Paragraphs

- Paragraphs are the building blocks of essays.

- You should be careful that each paragraph makes a point, and just one point.

- All the ideas of a paragraph should relate to that main point. What does not relate to the main point of a paragraph should be deleted.

- Each paragraph should support your overall thesis.

- There is no absolute right length for a paragraph; usually, the body-paragraphs should be half a page to one page long.

Keys to Paragraph Division

- Know what your paragraph is meant to do. (What point is this paragraph making?)

- Know how it affects your argument. (How does it contribute to your argument?)

Write the answers to these questions in your topic sentence which belongs at or near the beginning of your paragraph.

Transitions

Transition sentences and words between body paragraphs or inside body paragraphs function as bridges between your thoughts. Transition words and phrases such as *furthermore, therefore, first, thus, finally, in short, in addition, briefly, similarly, likewise, in the same way, however, nevertheless*, and *nonetheless* will keep ideas logically connected and make your writing clear and smooth. Transition sentences are even more effective than transition words because they continue your previous idea and introduce the next idea. Thus, make sure you use plenty of transition sentences and words in your essay. A "transitionless" paper is one that doesn't flow well and will not communicate your ideas effectively. An excellent resource for perfecting your use of transitions and organizing phrases is *They Say, I Say* by Gerald Graff and Cathy Birkenstein. You can also find support and word lists online

INTRODUCTION OR THE OPENING PARAGRAPH(S)

Your introduction is important because it sets the tone of your essay and makes your essay's first impression. You may want to start your essay with a narration or with a provocative quotation, anecdote, image, or fact. Make sure to present the subject and focus of the essay as directed by your assignment, write the names of the authors and the titles of texts under consideration, and work your way toward the thesis statement or essay plan. If you write about multiple authors, then mention the main sides and angles of your discussion instead of listing all their names. An important part of your introduction is the thesis statement, a sentence (or sentences) that usually closes your introduction.

Criteria for an Effective Introduction

- Hooks the reader

- Identifies the topic

- Establishes scope (you cannot cover the history of the world)

- States the names of the authors and titles of texts

- Gives important background information or context

- Contains the thesis

What Not to Do in the Introduction

- Begin with generalizations

- Provide obvious definitions

- Include platitudes or clichés: "From the beginning of this country...," "In today's society...," and "A picture is worth a thousand words"

- Give an apology or excuse (you should be the expert)

CONCLUSION

Your closing paragraph is also an important part of your essay and it is your chance to end in style and in control. Your conclusion should reinforce your argument and suggest additional ways of looking at the subject.

Criteria for a Good Conclusion

- Include a brief summary of the essay's main points
- Describe qualifications for your argument (i.e. limitations or other viewpoints)

- Call for some sort of action

- Suggest the results or consequences

- Propose possible approaches or solutions to the ideas raised

- State briefly a provocative issue for future study

- Address ideas from a fresh perspective in order to encourage the reader to continue thinking about the topic

- Include something from the introduction, such as a detail, image, or example, to bring the argument full circle

- Save a provocative, unexpected, or exciting insight or quotation for the conclusion

3.   DRAFTING

Because nobody gets it right the first time, you should write two, three, or more drafts and improve the quality of your paper with each one. When you write your drafts, keep in mind the assignment prompt, the purpose of the paper, and your audience. Focus on writing and putting ideas on paper in your first draft and remember that editing and revision are the last stages of the writing process. Do not give up and continue writing no matter how difficult it is and how uninspired and frustrated you feel at the moment. The pages will add up. If you do not want to write the introduction first, write middle paragraphs and return to the introduction later. You are in control of your own writing and writing process.

Let us consider some examples of drafts and look at the first and second drafts of two students. Both students write solid second drafts while their first drafts are not as good. The assignment prompt required students to summarize a text in one paragraph and write an argument about the same text in another paragraph.

In the first example, the student writes a brief summary and argument for the first draft and a more detailed and insightful summary and argument for the second draft.

Student One: First Draft

> In the paper "The Republic of Science: Its Political and Economic Theory" Michael Polanyi discusses the manner in which the world's collective scientific society evolves and regulates itself. Polanyi states that in science, both isolated work and controlled, coordinated work are ineffectual.

> If abstract or "selfish" fields of study are eliminated, critical pieces of the puzzle may not be found; and although all effort is being pooled to solve the problem, the confinement of research eliminates the possibility of the solution being found. So, science must be allowed to work at its own rapid rate, with no outside influence or confinement.

Student One: Second Draft

> In the paper "The Republic of Science: Its Political and Economic Theory" Michael Polanyi discusses the manner in which the world's collective scientific society evolves and regulates itself. Polanyi states that in science, both isolated work and controlled, coordinated work are ineffectual. Instead, the best method for progression is for each individual to build upon current ideas and previous theories, which in turn will lay the groundwork for future solutions (55). Polanyi adds that for science to advance, each individual must take on experiments that test the limits of their abilities. The experiment must have results that meet the criteria that determine scientific merit: satisfactory credibility, accuracy, and originality (56-57). These criteria define how a scientist must adhere to current beliefs while simultaneously challenging them. Polanyi finally states that scientists must seek scientific enlightenment to advance the collective knowledge of humanity (72-73).

> Michael Polanyi's argument is legitimate and well reasoned, and as he says, scientific advancement has been shown to flounder when restrictions are imposed, and to flourish when left to grow and evolve along its natural course. At times it may be appropriate for scientists to agree upon a course of study that specifically alleviates

current hardships, but no body of government or religion should attempt to decide when such actions should be taken. The way in which scientific discoveries occur depends on fluidly shared knowledge and upon seemingly unimportant or unrelated discoveries that are actually crucial to the eventual solution. If abstract or "selfish" fields of study are eliminated, critical pieces of the puzzle may not be found; and although all effort is being pooled to solve the problem, the confinement of research eliminates the possibility of the solution being found. So, science must be allowed to work at its own rapid rate, with no outside influence or confinement.

As we can see, the second draft of the first student is more detailed and the ideas are more developed and provocative. In the next example, the opposite happens. In his first draft, the second student wrote five paragraphs instead of two and repeated many ideas and words. His second draft, an improved version of the first draft, succeeds because it is concise and clear and it meets the criteria of the assignment. The draft avoids redundancy and presents an insightful argument in a straightforward way.

Student Two: First Draft

On January 28th 1986, the Space Shuttle Challenger was destroyed from its inability to perform in the colder conditions. The failure resulted in the loss of millions of dollars, but more importantly seven lives. Almost immediately, the public wanted to understand who was responsible for the failure. While the responsibility of the disaster falls primarily on management, all involved could have easily prevented the situation.

The disaster is the result of poor management in large. The engineers understood that the O-ring might and probably would fail; with that in mind, management decided to launch against the engineers' recommendations. While the engineers did not have concrete data to support their hypothesis, their concerns displayed so lividly should have been given more respect and due process. Since management did not heed the engineers' warnings, the management team is responsible for the financial loss and the even larger loss of life.

Even though management could be held responsible, the losses resulting from the O-ring failure are larger than who was technically responsible. The engineers were in a position to prevent the launch of the shuttle, and even though in hindsight it is easy to say what they should have done, there are several strategies that the engineers should have used regardless of the outcome of the launch. Primarily, the engineers should have made more effort to produce sufficient evidence and let the evidence speak for itself. No matter what the project is, this is always a necessary step, even more so at this scale of engineering. The engineers did not need to know that the shuttle would indeed fail to provide the necessary information to delay its launch.

With or without the sufficient evidence, the engineers should have employed better communication skills. When there is a table of vice presidents deciding whether to launch, becoming belligerent will rarely solve anything. The engineers should have controlled their emotions, looked at the issue from all sides, and presented an argument that was more persuasive in nature. For instance, the engineers could have explained that launching was not worth the millions of dollars and seven lives, because that potential failure would produce that result. Whatever the engineers did decide to say, their message needed to be clear, calm, and one of team work with the managers, not outright anger. Even though the managers are technically responsible, the engineers could have done more to prevent the disaster than they did.

Engineering projects require attention to every little component involved. Any project involving space requires this sort of attention on an order of many times more in magnitude. Because of the increased difficulties with space and the increased costs, anyone engineering space projects need to approach the project with a common mindset; the project must only be executed when it is ready to be executed, and speeding up this process must be done with great caution. Approaching the project from all sides united under this one ideal, and the disaster, like many other disasters, would have been another small event, seamlessly woven into the fabric of history.

Student Two: Second Draft

In Roger Boisjoly's "The Challenger Disaster: Moral Responsibility and the Working Engineer," engineering ethics are scrutinized against the hazards of making decisions based on inadequate morals. Boisjoly attempts to prevent the Challenger disaster on January 28, 1986, by protesting the launch to his superiors, a relatively unprecedented action to be taken by an engineer. The management team ignores his concerns, and proceeds to launch, which results in a financial loss of millions and a much more important human loss of seven lives. In response to the technical O-ring failure that he claims resulted from poor management and ethics, Boisjoly argues that the code of ethics engineers follow needs to be revised to protect the interests of human life, not the interests of the company an engineer works for (6-14).

While Boisjoly's revolution of engineering ethics is unprecedented and bold, engineers need to abide by yet an even higher level of ethics involving the strategies that could have averted this disaster. The skills engineers approach their careers with need to be broader than technical ability and moral obligation; engineers need to be well versed in communication, persuasion, and risk analysis. I agree that the management should not have launched and I believe they are to blame, but blame does not imply lone source of ability to prevent the disaster. The engineers could have, and I believe should have, worked harder to provide evidence, refused and protested the launch, and argued with the management team more effectively. Boisjoly did fight the good fight, but his barbaric communication skills undoubtedly impeded his argument. If he had approached management with a sense of camaraderie and used persuasion instead of brute force, this paper would probably not exist.

As we can see above, papers get better through several drafts, so it is important that students write these drafts to improve their quality of ideas, grammar, and editorial techniques.

How Do We Make Papers Longer?

If you wrote two, three drafts, you should be able to meet the page requirements of a paper. However, some papers are more difficult to write than others, so there may be times when you simply have nothing more to add. Usually, those are the times when you realize your paper is shorter than the required length. Here are some tips you can use to make your paper longer (or even help combat writer's block):

- Reread the assignment instructions and make sure you followed your professor's requirements.

- Make sure each paragraph is approximately half a page long. If your paragraphs are shorter than half a page, you need to go back and add more sentences.

- Do not forget to write authors' names and titles in the introduction.

- Reread your thesis statement and decide what else you need to add to make your thesis complex, detailed, and debatable.

- Ask yourself whether or not your thesis is supported well enough. If not, you need to think of a new idea and write a new paragraph to support your thesis.

- In some cases, you should do more research and find new evidence for the claims you are making.

- Write transition sentences and topic sentences for each body-paragraph. In other words, add at least two sentences to your body-paragraphs.

- Add more quotations and examples from the texts you are using to support your points. Equally important, explain and analyze the quotations you give.

- Reread the paper and find concepts and ideas that need more explanations. Remember that your audience does not know as much as you do about your topic, and thus, some ideas could be clarified further.

4. SUMMARY, PARAPHRASE, AND QUOTATION

We summarize information every day. For instance, if your friend missed class, she might ask what happened in her absence. You may give a simple summary: "We talked about the reading, took a quiz, and went over the next chapter," or a more substantial summary in which you explain the main points of the reading, what the quiz was on, and the major information in the new chapter. In any case, you will be covering main ideas, putting them in your own words, and condensing the information. While class may have lasted 50 minutes, your summary could last anywhere from a minute to several minutes. Unless you hate your classmate, are a compulsive liar, or want to mislead her because she is screwing up the curve, you will probably maintain fidelity to the real meaning of the class content. To sum up what I've been saying, **summary remains objective and true to the original's meaning but reduces the original's length**.

Paraphrasing, on the other hand, **consists of staying true to the original in both meaning and length**. We would never paraphrase a whole class. Paraphrase is often used when we want to explain something more clearly than the original author did or to help someone see it in a new way. It can be employed when translating text created for one audience into language suitable for another audience. For example, if you want a client to understand the details of an engineering report, you may need to paraphrase parts of it. You would paraphrase rather than summarize portions where the client needs to understand each and every detail. You may also paraphrase when you want your professor to know that you understand information in a particular passage of a reading.

You will want to **quote** from an original when you determine that you need the **exact wording of the author**, either because he is an expert and you want to wield his authority by showing how he articulated the information, because he worded his idea with such eloquence and economy that you would never be able to match, or because you want to analyze particular words and/or phrasings of the author. It is important to choose quotes with discernment; often people are tempted to quote more than necessary because it is easier to do than condensing ideas into summaries, or reworking details into paraphrases.

Let's look at some examples. First let's read an excerpt from "The Tragedy of the Commons," by Garrett Hardin. Then we'll look at a summary of it, a paraphrase of a portion of it, and determine which parts would be most quotable and why.

> In passing, it is worth noting that the morality of an act cannot be determined from a photograph. One does not know whether a man killing an elephant or setting fire to the grassland is harming others until one knows the total system in which his act appears. "One picture is worth a thousand words," said an ancient Chinese; but it may take 10,000 words to validate it. It is as tempting to ecologists as it is to reformers in general to try to persuade others by way of the photographic shortcut. But the essence of an argument cannot be photographed: it must be presented rationally—in words [1].

We could summarize this paragraph by saying, "A photograph is not a fair means of representing the complexities of an argument. Instead, words are the most efficient mode of showing persuasive elements of context and morality."

We would generally not go to the trouble of paraphrasing an entire paragraph. Let's choose a portion—the last two sentences—of it to explain more clearly. In paraphrasing we don't want to fall into the trap of copying the syntax of the original and inserting synonyms. Therefore, read the sentences and then look away from them when you write your paraphrase. This way the information may not remain in the same order or sentence units. "While pictures can be persuasive and may be a popular tool for those who want to affect change, they run the risk of oversimplifying a given situation. Words, which show logical relationships, present the truest meaning of an argument."

The original ran about three lines and so does this paraphrase. Both the original and my paraphrase are structured in two sentences— though the information is not in the same order. While the paraphrases uses different forms of the same words—"persuade" becomes "persuasive"; "presented" becomes "present"— in very few instances are the exact words used in both versions. Does the paraphrase remain true to Hardin's meaning? That is a primary goal of paraphrase. Paraphrase and summary are not the place for the writer to insert his or her own views.

Which parts might you want quote? Which parts are worded most distinctly, are most rich with linguistic flavor? One good possibility is the second sentence in which Hardin offers a vivid example of what may go wrong when relying on a photograph to convey more than it is able: "One does not know whether a man killing an elephant or setting fire to the grassland is harming others until one knows the total system in which his act appears." In order to use the quote while making a point about what Hardin is arguing here, the writer needs to contextualize the quote with an author tag such as "Hardin argues," and in what some people call a "sandwich": introduce the quote, quote, comment on the quote's significance to the point you are making. The writer's comments make up the bread, the quote is the thinly sliced roast beef, the soft havarti, or the marinated tofu. Let's take a look at what this would look like:

Hardin warns of a photograph's limitations in conveying moral information when he writes, "One does not know whether a man killing an elephant or setting fire to the grassland is harming others until one knows the total system in which his act appears." In this statement he calls into question the reliability of the adage that a picture is worth a thousand words by showing how much information is missing from a single snapshot of a situation.

Finally, here are some strategies to keep in mind when faced with the tasks of summarizing, paraphrasing, and quoting. Before we list the strategies, however, let's look at why the strategies are useful.

Let's work with a new passage, this time from the first chapter of *The Elements of Moral Philosophy* by James Rachels, which virtually every NHV student of all time has read and will read. Here are more examples of summarizing, paraphrasing, and quoting. Identify what, if anything, is going wrong in the work. Then we'll cull some basic rules of thumb.

It would be nice if there were a simple recipe for constructing good arguments and avoiding bad ones. Unfortunately, there is no easy method. Arguments can go wrong in an indefinite number of ways, as is evident from the various arguments about the handicapped babies; and one must always be alert to the possibility of new complications and new kinds of error. But that is not surprising. The rote application of routine methods is never a satisfactory substitute for critical intelligence, in any area. Moral thinking is no exception [2, p. 13].

Check out these summaries. What do you think of them?

As Rachels points out, there isn't a good recipe for setting up solid arguments [2, p. 13].

Rachels asserts that there should be a set formula for composing sound arguments that successfully address relevant complexities, but there isn't [2, p. 13].

Rachels notes that setting up arguments is a complicated task requiring awareness of pertinent viewpoints and of potential inaccuracies in thinking; for instance, some people thinks parents should determine what should happen to babies born with extreme birth defects and others feels these decisions should be determined by laws. Therefore, a simple argument proving what is right or wrong is not easy to devise [2, p. 13].

SUMMARIZING STRATEGIES

Address the original's whole meaning:

Explain the claim **and** the reasons given to support the claim: there isn't a set procedure for setting up an argument **because** it is too complex of a task.

Maintain accuracy and objectivity:

In a summary we want to represent the information provided by the author, not put in our own views or judgments. Rachels does not say there "should" be a formula for composing arguments. Really, he says there shouldn't be one.

Focus on the main ideas, not details and examples:

In a summary we are addressing the ideas, not the details. In this case, the various viewpoints regarding who should make decisions about the lives of handicapped babies should not be mentioned. Here is an example:

Unfortunately, there is not a formula for creating effective and convincing arguments. Instead, critical thinking is required in order to identify flaws in reasoning and nuanced meaning in complex situations such as those involving determinations of morality.

Cite all summarized information:

Be sure to give credit to the source from which the information in your summary came.

Now let's look at some paraphrases of the first couple of sentences.

It would be nice if there were a simple recipe for constructing good arguments and avoiding bad ones. Unfortunately, there is no easy method.

What do you think about them?

Rachels observes that it would be nice if there were a simple recipe for constructing good arguments and avoiding bad ones. Unfortunately, there is no easy method [2, p. 13].

Rachels admits that it would be convenient if there were a simple formula for building sound arguments and not building weak ones. The bad news is, there isn't a simple technique [2, p. 13].

Rachels insists that strong arguments are not constructed by predetermined formulas, but that writers must refrain from making poor arguments. A sound argument is not impossible to compose [2, p. 13].

Rachels asserts the brutal truth that arguments are difficult to write well and that there are many ways weak reasons destroy solid argumentation [2, p. 13].

PARAPHRASING STRATEGIES

Use synonyms:

"recipe" can become "procedure" or "formula"

"good" can become "solid," "strong," or "sound"

"easy" can become "simple"

Change word order:

"It would be convenient if there were a simple formula to build sound arguments and avoid weak ones" can become "A formula that avoids weak arguments and builds sound ones would be convenient"

Change word forms:

"constructing," can become "constructed"

"avoiding" can become "avoid"

Maintain the tone of the original:

Avoid using unnecessarily charged words like "brutal" and "destroy"

Change point of clarification forms:

"Strong arguments are not constructed by predetermined formulas and require hard work to construct" can become "Although we wish for easy techniques for writing flawless arguments, strong argumentation is a complex and difficult task" in which "we" as agents take a more central role in the sentence.

Use key words:

The idea of what is involved in creating well-constructed arguments is key to this excerpt. Using the word "argument" in your paraphrase will assist in maintaining clarity and precision. There is not a better way to express the concept of argument.

Cite all paraphrases:

Be sure to give credit to the source from which the information in your paraphrase came. This can be done with a combination of information in your sentence and a bracketed citation: "As James Rachels argues in his book,

The Elements of Moral Philosophy,...[p. 13] or simply with a bracketed citation: [2, p. 13].

Here are some examples of things that can go wrong while incorporating quotes. What can be improved in the following examples?

Rachels notes that arguments can go wrong in an indefinite number of ways [2, p. 13].

"Unfortunately there is no easy method" of "constructing good arguments," according to Rachels [2, p. 13].

Rachels shows there are many views regarding what should happen with babies who are born with severe birth defects. "Moral thinking is no exception [2, p. 13].

QUOTING STRATEGIES

Be sure to use quotation marks when quoting:

Rachels notes, "Arguments can go wrong in an indefinite number of ways" [2, p. 13].

Choose quotes carefully:

Be sure that there is something distinctive about the language or meaning that you can only address by using a quote. "Unfortunately there is no easy method" should be paraphrased, not quoted, since there is nothing special about this wording.

Introduce your quotes:

Be sure that your readers know exactly why you have included the quote so they are clear about what they should look for in it. Part of our jobs in introducing a quote is giving it proper context so that the reader understands what the quote means in the original text, like this: Although it would be convenient if there were formulaic ways to prove our points, Rachels argues that critical thinking is always required in constructing arguments and that "Moral thinking is no exception" [2, p. 13].

Comment on the significance of the quote and how it supports the point you are making:

> After your quote, be sure to explain how it helps you make your point. Following the above quote, "Moral thinking is no exception," one could explain it this way: In fact, because of the tendency to have strong feelings about many moral situations, making moral arguments may require even more critical thinking than other sorts of persuasion.

Cite all quotes:

> Be sure to give credit to the source from which the information in your quote came. This can be done with a combination of information in your sentence and a bracketed citation: "As James Rachels argues in his book, *The Elements of Moral Philosophy*,…" [2, p. 13] or simply with a bracketed citation: [2, p. 13].

References

[1]   G. Hardin,"The Tragedy of the Commons," http://www.garretthardinsociety.org/articles/art_tragedy_of_the _commons.html Accessed Jan. 22, 2010.

[2]   J. Rachels, *The Elements of Moral Philosophy*, 4th ed. Boston: McGraw Hill, 2003.

5.   REVISION

Revision does not mean changing a few words, adding some commas, and writing a new title. Do not waste your time and your teacher's if you want to take the easy way out and spend ten minutes revising your paper. In fact, many writers spend more time revising a paper than writing it. Your goal is to improve the quality of your paper altogether starting with your argument, continuing with the support of your argument in your body paragraphs, and ending with grammatical and editorial issues.

Thus, the errors in grammar, spelling, punctuation, and mechanics need to be fixed, but they should not be your only concern. Your argument, its support, your analysis of the texts, and the quality of your ideas will constitute your main focus of the revision process. Below you will find examples of original papers and revised ones and some guidelines on how to revise and what you should focus on when you revise.

REVISING CONTENT

Revision offers vast opportunities for improving one's writing. Have you ever realized after writing your whole paper that you need to change your thesis? And once you change your thesis, some points in your paper need to be fine-tuned, as well? But the truth is, the paper is due in the morning and you need to get some sleep. Many of us do not make necessary revisions because of lack of time or lack of awareness. Sometimes we don't realize that our logic and style are not entirely clear until we receive feedback from our peers and instructors.

In the following example of a summary and response paper, generally the first major paper assigned in Nature and Human Values, one student, whom we'll call Jamie, turned in a response to Aldo Leopold's "The Land Ethic," a chapter from his book, *A Sand County Almanac*. The logic of the paper is unclear in places. For example, how some of the quotations taken from "The Land Ethic" actually support Jamie's points isn't obvious to the reader. The paper, as a whole, lacks clear focus, and Jamie's ultimate point is uncertain.

Fortunately, Jamie is a very hard worker, opts to revise the paper, and makes some impressive improvements. First, read Jamie's initial version, and then read her revised paper. What kinds of changes do you expect in a revision? What changes do you notice in Jamie's revision? If Jamie were to revise the paper again, what suggestions would you offer?

First Draft of Jamie's Response to an Argument

In the "Land Ethic" Aldo Leopold argues that earth needs to be thought of and taken care of. He explains in his essay how the earth should be treated as one of the community members. He gives examples of different viewpoints of property and the use of the land and how the land changed over the times. He begins his paper talking about how the slave-girls in ancient Greece were treated as property. The slave-girls were killed for their misbehavior. He then shows how that was considered normal back then, but now it is not. Leopold ties together the slave girls with how we need to change our state of thinking of the land not just as property but as a member of society. He states a good argument on how the earth should be thought of and treated as a citizen. Although, I agree with Leopold on some of his points such as how we should start taking care of the land but I disagree with thinking of the land as a member of society. We should take care of the land and learn to reuse it, but I have an issue with Leopold's belief that the land should be treated as an equal.

Leopold brings ethics into the picture by talking about how we should reuse the land and how we should think of the future of the land. He paints a picture of how the land has been used over the past. Wars have been fought on it, food has been grown on it, and resources have been taken from it. The land has been exploited and it starts to make an ugly picture with everything that has happened with the contamination and pollution that goes into it daily. Leopold contends with "Transportation brings about another basic change: the plants or animals grown in one region are now consumed and returned to the soil in the rocks" [1, p. 136]. In the end, we are part of the ground. After our time we go into the ground and we become the soil and then it takes nutrients back from our bodies. I don't want to become part of the land with the pollution, I would rather be a part of land that was cleaner.

He has brought to mind that the land should be thought of as a person not as property. Leopold points out "We can be ethical only in relation to something we can see, feel, understand, love, or otherwise have faith in" [1, p. 134]. I believe that for something to be considered as a human it should be a human. The earth does show life with the plants, water, and the life that live on it but I don't think it should be considered as a person. A person has emotions, thoughts, a soul, and feelings. To me a human life is a person born of a human who has dreams and ideas and thoughts

The land, however, is a means of life that we live off of. And the land is a way of life that we need to thrive off of. Everyone needs the land to live, so everyone is dependent on the land. The land is our home and our way of life, but it is not something that of life; it is something that contributes to life.

Leopold also talks about the life of the world being a huge pyramid. He suggests that "Each successive layer depends on those below it for food and often for other services" [1, p. 135]. Each one is dependent on the other. We are dependent on what the land has to give us. Without the land we wouldn't have the resources that we need to survive. We need everything that the world has to offer us. That is the way life is on earth. Every human, animal and plant is a part of the pyramid, but it's the land that takes care of us and gives us what we need to survive.

I believe that land does need to be taken care of and thought about how it is going to be used in the future. But the idea of it being considered as a human life is not logical in any sense. Humans can feel, learn, and explore the inter-workings of life. The land is a source of means that we will need throughout the lifetime that we are alive. We do need to consider the earth and its future possibilities because that is what shapes the future for living beings. In that way I believe what Leopold is saying in his essay, but the idea of the earth being the same as you and me is a long stretch. Leopold has a great view, but some of his ideas and thoughts I do not believe in. The definition of life is different for everyone, but the fact that life needs to live will never change.

Revised Version of Jamie's Response to an Argument

In the essay "The Land Ethic," Aldo Leopold argues that earth needs be more than just land, it needs to be thought of in a different state of mind. He explains in his essay how the earth should be treated as one of the community members. Leopold gives examples of the different viewpoints of property and the use of the land and how the land changed over the times. Leopold begins his essay by talking about how the slave-girls in ancient Greece were treated as property and how they were killed for their misbehavior.

That idea of slave-girls as property was considered normal back in ancient Greece, but it would be unethical to own a slave in America. Leopold ties together the slave-girls with how we need to change our state of thinking of the land, not just as property but as a member of society. My issue with this belief of Leopold is I see the meaning behind the state of thinking differently than he does.

Leopold explains this relationship by saying, "Your true modern is separated from the land by many middlemen, and by innumerable physical gadgets. He has no vital relation to it; to him it is the space between cities on which crops grow" [1, p. 139]. In this quote he explains how many things actually keep us from touching or being close with the land itself. Farmers for instance, have tractors and fancy equipment to do the dirty work for them, touching nothing but a machine, and keeping their hands clean. Leopold wants us to get down and dirty, to feel the earth and everything that is a part of it. He believes that if we can feel it like we do another person, the bond will grow between us and the land.

I believe we need to be with the land and utilize it for food, beauty, and learning. However, I disagree with Leopold's reasoning why we need to do so. To me it is important to use your hands to develop food from the land, and to get dirty not so we can have a deeper meaning of the land like we do a person, but just to do something the hard way. It is like opening your eyes to a different light. You develop an appreciation of those machines to cut the time in half it would have taken to do with your hands. Also, we can gain admiration for what the land has given us, and we need to know what it feels like to be covered in dirt. No human is perfectly clean; sometimes getting dirty is just human nature. It is a learning experience with the land. I also understand that the farmers need the equipment to keep producing enough crops to feed the earth's population and that is important. However, using your hands to work creates a type of connection I believe Leopold is trying to explain for different reasons than mine.

Likewise, the land can teach us deeper meanings. Leopold explains how we should consider the land. He writes, "We can be ethical only in relation to something we can see, feel, understand, love, or otherwise have faith in" [1, p. 134]. This quote means that we can have a relationship with something that isn't human. It is like having an emotional attachment to something that can't express emotions as human do. Leopold believes that this is important for humans to encounter this kind of emotion with the land.

I believe we should have some kind of attachment to the land, just not the same type as Leopold explains. To me, we should all have a relationship with the land to explore and learn. The 2000 Webster Dictionary defines relationship as a state of connectedness between people. We can have a state of connectedness with the land. Connectedness can come through a type of giving: we give to the land and the land gives back. Everyone needs to be alone with nature, not to love it as we would our own sister, but to love it as land. We can love many things but the love between humans is far greater than the love we share with the land. It is a stretch to have the same type of love for land that we do for family. The love I share with the land is more of a spiritual and intrapersonal bonding. Just being in nature away from the everyday city revises my mind and helps balance my everyday schedule. It helps me breathe and re-focus so when I do return to the city I am in a better state of mind. By that meaning I feel more energized for my everyday life. That is the relationship I believe everyone should share with the land.

Leopold talks about life on earth as a huge pyramid, he suggests, "Each successive layer depends on those below it for food and often for other services" [1, p. 135]. He explains that the land and humans are intertwined and each one is dependent on the other. The land depends on us to keep it healthy, meaning it is easier to destroy the land but it is harder to keep it useful. The land depends on us to keep it useful. It can be useful for food, learning, exploring, and living. As we learn about the land we find different ways we can replenish it. For example, flowers depend on the bees for pollination, and bees depend on flowers for pollen. If one gives less than one is expected then it offsets the balance. Just as much as we need the earth, it also needs us to collect its "pollen." Also, we build our homes on the land and the dirt. We depend on the land to hold our home. In a way the land is a part of the community as a home, since it is the structure that holds homes. We need to take care of our home, since it takes care of us. Without the land we wouldn't have the resources that we need to survive. We need everything that the earth has to offer us. Every human, animal and plant is a part of the pyramid, but it's the land that takes care of us and gives us what we need to survive.

I believe that land does need to have a relationship with humans, though not the same as Leopold suggests in his essay. It is important to have this bond for a clear state of mind to deal with everyday life. It is important to touch, feel and be alone with the land to develop the bond and love as Leopold proposes. Without this bond we wouldn't have this deeper relationship with the land and everything it offers us such as our food. We don't have this same bond with our family, friends, and other humans. They are two separate types of love which can never be the same. Otherwise, people would regard dirt with the same status as their neighbor.

REVISING SENTENCES

First draft sentences are usually wordy. Revising sentences to be more direct and economical makes your point more clearly to the reader. In the following example, revising sentences removes almost 50% of the words without any loss of meaning. If you can say the same thing in sentences of 40 words and of 25 words, use the sentence of 25 words.

Original Version:

The thing that Hardin's essay does is to explore the kinds of limits and obligations of human behavior that exist or should exist. It is an environmental argument he is making but from an economical point of view. His argument is that when it comes to communal resources we all share such as water or the air humanity is motivated more by his greed and self interest than by the necessity of doing what is best for everybody. He makes the claim that the benefit we might receive is only to that one person who is involved but the detriment of the action is one that is shared by everybody. Because of the vast difference that exists between the reward and the cost of an action man is motivated to not conserve anything at all but rather consume as much resources and make as much money as possible as soon as possible. Hardin's point is that the population of our world as it exists today continues to grow at a rapid rate of speed but the resources are not changing at all especially due to the fact that when man destroys the environment around us in his haste to horde all of its resources. His argument is for population control because of the reality that the more people that are depending on the environment and nature for natural resources the more strain there will be and the more the environment has to endure. Hardin wants both for the government to regulate and control private industry and for the placing of restrictions to limit breeding. He goes on to comment that if the government of a nation has the responsibility to try and prevent environmental degradation of nature and overpopulation of the planet by humans. (294 words)

Revised Version:

Hardin's essay explores the limits and obligations of human behavior, making an environmental argument from an economic perspective. He argues that, when it comes to communal resources such as water or air, we are motivated more by greed and self interest than by the greater good. He claims that the potential benefit to overusing resources is an individual one but that the detriment of the action is shared by all. Thus, because of the vast difference between the reward and the cost of an action, we are motivated not to conserve but rather to consume as many resources and make money as quickly as we can. Maintaining that the global population continues to grow rapidly but that resources are not improving, he reasons that population control is necessary as the strain on resources and our environment grows. He concludes that government has the responsibility to prevent environmental degradation and overpopulation of the planet by not only regulating private industry but also by restricting breeding. (164 words)

REVISION GUIDELINES

The three revision guidelines below, Global and Local Revision, Revision Checklist, and Editing Checklist, will help you revise your essays and focus on the content—the ideas, and argument of your paper—and on grammar.

GLOBAL REVISION

1. After reading your teacher's and your peers' comments, set the essay aside for at least a day. When you come back to it, imagine yourself as a first-time reader of this text and imagine that you are someone who disagrees with the main argument of the essay. Be as grumpy as you can, always demanding more evidence, reluctant to change your mind.

2. Answer some or all of the following questions on a separate sheet of paper:

- If you were publishing this piece in a magazine, what kind of magazine would it be? What headline, photo, or illustration might accompany it to get your readers' attention?

- If you have to make a choice about this issue what would you choose?

- What's the main point you want to argue in this essay?

- What does the average member of this audience already know or believe about this topic?

- What would you want to tell a family member or friend of yours about this topic?

Now make one or more of the following revisions:

- Incorporate your answer to A or D into an introductory hook for your essay.

- Incorporate language from your answers to C or E into your thesis sentence.

- Incorporate ideas from your answers to B into your conclusion.

3. Write out your argumentative thesis. Circle 5-7 key words that clearly conver your argument. Write these words out on a separate piece of paper, and compare them to the starts and ends of your body paragraphs. Be sure that 2-3 of these words—or close synonyms—are easily visible in the opening and/or closing sentences as a reminder to your reader of your main argument.

4. In the margin next to each body paragraph, finish the sentence "This paragraph's main function is to prove [or demonstrate] that...." Then check the opening and closing sentences of the paragraphs: where necessary, include the exact language of your margin comment to help focus the paragraph.

5. Add two more quotations or facts to support claims in your essay. Now read your essay through quickly three times, focusing just on the quotations. On the first read-through, check to be sure that every quotation is introduced. Do not leave even a single "flying quotation" in the essay. On the second read, check to make sure every quotation is properly cited with parenthetical MLA, APA, or IEEE citations, and that the punctuation is correct for each one. For the third reading, slow down a bit: is each quotation followed by a "translation" sentence or a sentence that directly explains its connection to your argument using one or more key words from your thesis?

6. Reread your conclusion. Underline the sentence or two that most clearly makes your point. Compare this sentence to your introduction: if the conclusion sentence is clearer, "transplant" it to your introduction, which needs maximum clarity of argument. Then rewrite a sentence for your conclusion. Remember to answer your reader's question, "So, what?" by giving a recommendation, a call to action, and/or an explanation of how your ideas are important in the larger discussion of issues or efforts to change the system.

LOCAL REVISION

1. In four places in your essay, either combine two short sentences into one to smooth the ideas out, or split one long sentence into two sentences to make the ideas clearer.

2. In four places in your essay, switch a passive or weak verb (is, are, was, have, has, do) to the appropriate active verb, rewriting the sentence for a stronger punch.

3. In four places in your essay, replace a weak verb (particularly "feels" or "thinks") with a stronger, more interesting one ("claims . . . argues . . . explains").

4. Add three more transitional words/phrases to sentences at the starts or finishes of paragraphs. Then add 3 more transitional words/phrases to sentences in the middles of paragraphs.

5. Find any phrase that says "I think" or "In my opinion." If you are not giving a specific personal example from your experience, delete that phrase: make the argument stand on its own.

6. In two places in your essay, trim a quotation by 3-7 words; work the author's best phrases into your own sentence.

REVISION CHECKLIST

Adapted from Frederick Crews, *Handbook for Writers*

- Do I have a clear, properly limited, and interesting thesis?
- Have I provided adequate evidence for my thesis?
- Have I dealt with probable objections to my thesis?
- Is my thesis conspicuously stated? (Can you physically point to it?)
- Are my voice, stance, and tone appropriate to my audience and purpose?
- Have I supplied all necessary documentation and followed a standard form for doing so?
- Are my paragraphs unified and fully developed?
- Does my first paragraph attract the reader's attention?
- Have I made clear and helpful transitions between paragraphs?
- Does my last paragraph give enough sense of completion?

- Does my title indicate that I have a definite point to make?
- Are my sentences distinct, with effective subordination of minor elements?
- Do my sentences show enough emphasis and variety of structure?
- Do all of my words mean what I think they mean?
- Is my language appropriate to the occasion?
- Is my language vivid, concise, and imaginative?
- Have I kept to standard written usage?
- Does my punctuation bring out my meaning?
- Have I followed correct form for quoting other people's words?
- Have I looked up the spelling and hyphenation of doubtful words?
- Have I followed the correct form for capitals, italics, abbreviations, and numbers?

EDITING CHECKLIST

- Have you read the work aloud to listen for problems?
- Have you let a friend, relative, instructor, or Writing Center staff member read it to make sure it makes sense?
- Did you check every possible misspelling in a dictionary or with a spell checker?
- Did you edit for run-on sentences and comma splices?
- Did you edit for sentence fragments?
- Did you check your use of verbs?
- Did you check your use of pronouns?
- Did you check your use of modifiers?
- Have you checked any punctuation you are unsure of?
- Have you checked your use of capital letters?
- Have you used the right form of these words?

there / their / they're
to / too / two
its / it's
are / our
your / you're
we're / where / were
whose / who's
your / you're
than / then
accept / except
advise / advice
affect / effect
lose / loose
alright / all right

Chapter 6. ARGUMENTATION

1. ARGUMENTS

If someone—say, a friend of yours—states that he or she likes the town of Golden, Colorado, you have a limited number of responses. You can tell your friend that you didn't know that before. You can observe that many people like the town. You can state that you also like the town or that you don't. That's it. That's the end of the conversation and time for a new topic.

If, however, your friend states that Golden, Colorado, is one of the best college towns in the U.S., it's the beginning of a discussion, and the first response is naturally, "Why do you think that?" The response to your question will be a series of statements—"It feels like a small town, but it's close to a major city" or "The mesas and foothills are beautiful"—meant to support the first statement.

Note that when your friend says, "I like Golden," it is purely an expression of **personal preference** or **personal opinion**. You are free to express your personal preference, which may be the same or very different from your friend's. But the statement makes no claim on you; it has to do only with your friend. In contrast, the statement "Golden is one of the best college towns" is a public assertion, and it makes an implicit claim on you: "This is a judgment, but it is a well-considered judgment, and I present it for your agreement or disagreement." A claim that promises support and that asks for agreement or disagreement is an **arguable assertion**.

An **argument** is nothing more than an arguable assertion along with its support, the answers to the question "Why?" The **conclusion** of an argument is the public claim offered for agreement or disagreement; it is the debatable assertion that, implicitly or explicitly, the person making the argument hopes to persuade you is right. The **reasons**—sometimes called

79

premises—are the additional statements made to answer the question "Why do you think that?" and to logically lead you to accept the conclusion.

"Conclusion" sounds like it should come at the end, but often a conclusion is asserted at the start of an argument. A conclusion is a conclusion because it logically *follows* from the reasons. Here's a very simple argument:

> We should all ride bicycles more. Bicycles don't pollute. Bicycling can improve health.

The first statement is clearly the one that is being presented to persuade and to change our behavior. It is the conclusion, and the other two statements are the premises. If we arranged the argument in logical order, it would look like this:

> P1: Bicycles don't pollute.
>
> P2: Bicycling can improve health.
>
> C: We should all ride bicycles more.
>
> ("P" stands for "Premise," and "C" for "Conclusion.")

As it stands, the argument is incomplete; there are logical steps missing. That doesn't mean the argument is necessarily faulty. Most arguments assume logical steps and leave it to the hearer or reader to fill them in. Sometimes those **assumptions** are non-controversial, but sometimes they are not. Let's fill in the steps:

> P1A: Bicycles don't pollute.
>
> P1B: We should do whatever we can to reduce pollution.
>
> P2A: Bicycling can improve health.
>
> P2B: We should do whatever we can to improve our health.
>
> C: We should all ride bicycles more.

We actually have parallel arguments here: P1A and P2A lead logically to the conclusion, and P2A and P2B also lead logically to the conclusion. Either argument alone might be convincing, but both together may be even more so. Note that P1A and P2A are facts; they are truthful assertions. Of course, it's possible to nit-pick. Someone might object to P2A on the grounds that sending a blind person off on a bicycle would probably mean injury rather than health. When we interpret assertions, however, we apply what logicians call the **principle of charity**; we take them in the sense they were probably intended and in the most reasonable sense. According to the principle of charity, "Bicycling can improve heath" really means "For most human beings, excluding those who are sight-impaired or have other sorts of medical conditions that would render the activity dangerous to themselves or others, regular bicycling can improve health." Similarly, under the principle of charity, an objection to P1A such as "Bicycles equipped with mechanisms that spray DDT and other harmful substances into the air do in fact pollute" is not a serious objection.

P1B and P2B, the assumptions of the argument, are not facts; they are themselves argumentative assertions, and we could ask for reasoned support for each one. But a full argument for P1B and P2B isn't really necessary. Most people, perhaps a very large majority, would accept both. These claims are not factual, but since they are widely accepted as valid, they have almost the same force as facts. Reasons offered in a strong argument may be either facts or generally acceptable judgments.

Our argument is a relatively strong one. First, if you accept the premises, you'd have a hard time rejecting the conclusion. Second, the stated premises are true as facts, and the assumptions are widely believed. Does the fact that this argument is a fairly strong one mean that everyone will accept the reasons, the assumptions, or the conclusions? No matter how strong the argument, there may be some people who will reject it. Most arguments do not command assent in the same way that mathematical proofs or well-founded scientific theories do. Some arguments lead to heated debate and controversy. But there are arguments that are so strong that agreement is general and wide-spread: "Slavery is wrong"; "Women should have civil equality"; "Every citizen in a democracy should be able to vote." There was a time when many people—and perhaps even a majority of people—disagreed with each of those assertions, but the arguments against those conclusions proved so weak, and those for the conclusions so strong, that now we have almost universal agreement.

Argumentation is not simply a way of supporting our claims and seeking to bring others into agreement. It is also a way of testing our own beliefs and attitudes and values to see if they have sufficient backing. Arguments are made in the context of other arguments. Every argument is a response to one or more other arguments. Arguments are part of a dialogue, a conversation. In that dialogue, you make your argument and see how well it fares in relation to competing arguments. If your argument has little or weak support compared to opposing arguments, that's probably a sign that it's time for re-thinking and re-evaluation. Even if your argument appears strong, chances are good that exposure to other arguments with different conclusions will lead you to modify some of your reasons.

Argumentative conversation need not be hostile or impolite. In fact, hostility and rudeness in debate are often signs that rational debate is not taking place. People often resort to insult, childish sarcasm, and name-calling when they suspect that the views they have embraced do not in fact have good support. In real argumentation, statements are likely to begin "That's a good point, but . . ." or "I can see your point, but here's why I disagree . . ." or "Yes, that's true, but I don't think it's relevant because . . ." Argumentative dialogue is a collaboration; we enlist the aid of our opponents to test our arguments so that we can improve them, modify them, or perhaps give them up. The goal of debate is to arrive at the best conclusions supported by the best reasons. It is, in other words, a central part of progress toward rationality.

To be **biased** is to have a view that either has no substantial logical support or has bad support. For example, if I assert that the last part of the freeway around Denver, presently not complete, should be constructed through the town of Golden, and if my primary reason is that I have stock in a highway construction company that could get a profitable contract, my argument is biased. The conclusion that the highway should be built *simply because* I will profit does not follow logically and will persuade no one. Biased arguments may make a show of logic, but the motivating reasons will be matters of personal profit, simple prejudice, or blind ideology. When the hidden reasons are revealed, a biased argument collapses.

Of course, everyone has biases. We all have assumptions about the world and the people in it that we've inherited and that make it possible to go about living our lives. If we had to stop and rationally evaluate every conclusion we draw in daily life, we'd be immobilized. Normally, those biases do little harm. If one of my operating assumptions is that people in black and white cars with lights on the top are all out to get me if I violate the speed limit by even a bit, that assumption may be entirely wrong, but it does motivate me to slow down when I see highway patrol cars, and it may have saved me a ticket or two. Some biases, however, do need rational testing. If one of my fundamental assumptions is that women cannot do advanced mathematics, that bias may have unfortunate results in my speech and actions, and it deserves to be rationally tested and then rejected.

Why does argumentation matter? At the end of a trial, when the prosecuting or defense attorney rises to make a closing statement to the jury, he or she is making an argument. The premises for that argument are the evidence and testimony presented earlier in the trial. And the logical soundness of that argument can make a great deal of difference for the defendant. When a politician speaks, he or she makes an argument for certain policies; the logical soundness of that argument may persuade voters, and the policies implemented may make a great deal of difference to millions. When an engineer stands before a client and asserts that a project should or should not be built—or should be built one way and not another way—he or she is making an argument with scientific and mathematical backing, but it is still an argument, and the result matters.

Earlier, we suggested that ethical philosophy holds that the most moral course of action is that which has the best reasons supporting it. In this chapter, we have been focused on argumentation. Now we can bring the two concerns of NHV together: ethical action is defined by the best argument. It might have seemed that NHV was divided between the content of the course—engineering and ethics—and the skills taught—writing and argumentation. The content and the skill are the same: thinking about ethics means finding the best arguments.

2. KINDS OF ARGUMENT

Traditionally, arguments are divided into two kids: **deductive** and **inductive**. Deductive arguments aim at the rigor of a mathematical proof, and a strong deductive argument commands agreement. That is, the only way you can disagree with a strong deductive argument is by giving up logic entirely and admitting you are not entirely sane. Here's one old, traditional example of a deductive argument:

> P1: All men are mortal.
>
> P2: Socrates is a man.
>
> C: Socrates is mortal.

The argument's not terribly earth-shaking, but it is rigorously logical. When a deductive argument is logical, we say that it is **valid**. To say that an argument is valid is to say that, *if* the reasons are true, the conclusion *has to be true*. When an argument is valid, once you accept the reasons, you have to accept the conclusion.

Logical validity, however, is not enough for the argument to be a sound argument. It's perfectly easy to construct a valid argument with one or more untrue reasons. Here's one:

> P1: Everything that has a moon is a shoebox.
>
> P2: The earth has a moon.
>
> C: The earth is a shoebox.

The argument is valid: if you accept P1 and P2, you have to accept C. Statement P2 is, of course, true, and P1 is obviously false. While this argument is valid, it is not sound because one of its premises is untrue. A **sound** deductive argument meets two conditions; 1) it is valid, and 2) the premises are true. An unsound argument will either be invalid or have untrue premises. In the case of a really bad deductive argument, the conclusion does not logically follow from the reasons and the reasons are mostly or entirely untrue.

We can change our valid but unsound argument a bit:

P1: Every shoebox has a moon.

P2: The earth is a shoebox.

C: The earth has a moon.

In this case, the argument is still valid, but both premises are untrue. The conclusion, however, just happens to be true. The truth of the conclusion means nothing in terms of the soundness of the argument. But sound arguments are required to *prove* the truth of conclusions.

Consider this argument:

P1: Fred lives in Vail.

C: Fred is a skier.

The argument contains an unstated assumption, and we easily supply it:

P1: Fred lives in Vail.

P2: Everyone who lives in Vail is a skier.

C: Fred is a skier.

Now the argument is complete and deductively valid, but it's obviously unsound. Even if we apply the principle of charity and interpret P2 to mean "Everyone who lives in Vail is a skier or a snowboarder," there has to be at least one person living in Vail who does not ski or board. To disprove a universal statement ("Everyone who lives in Vail is a skier." or "All men are mortal."), only a single counter example is necessary.

Let's modify the argument a bit:

P1: Fred lives in Vail.

C: Fred is probably a skier.

The implied reason now is this: P2:"Most people who live in Vail are skiers." We now have a much more acceptable argument, one that most people would find fairly convincing. Arguments based on probability, rather than logical necessity, are **inductive** arguments.

We never say that inductive arguments are valid since "valid" suggests logical necessity, and inductive arguments never rise to that standard. Instead we say that inductive arguments are more or less

forceful. If an argument is inductively forceful, the conclusion follows from the reasons with reasonable probability. To put it another way, if I accept the reasons offered in a forceful inductive argument, I have to admit that it's reasonable to accept that the conclusion is probably true. Conversely, if I accept the reasons offered in an argument but see that the conclusion does not probably follow from the reasons, then I can say the argument is inductively weak. Further, if the argument is forceful, and if the reasons are in fact true (or generally acceptable), then the argument is inductively **sound**.

Most real-world arguments deal with probabilities and are largely inductive. The debate over health care reform, for example, turns on the probable results of adopting or rejecting changes in policy. No one can predict the future with complete accuracy, and so deductive argument on this topic is impossible. But we can make reasonable claims about what will probably happen as a result of a policy change.

The sample arguments we've looked at are fairly trivial examples, useful only to help us get a sense of how rational argument works at a very basic level. Real-world arguments are much more complex, and while it is possible to take the argument made in a political speech or a newspaper editorial and to break it down into first-order premises, intermediate conclusions (assertions established by argument that serve as reasons for further conclusions), and the final argumentative conclusion, with each line of reasoning evaluated in terms of deductive and inductive soundness, that rarely happens. Logicians may analyze (and diagram) arguments at the microscopic level, but most people do not.

In the real world of argument, no one says or writes, "This argument, while valid, is finally unsound" or "This argument rests on an unstated assumption whose truth is questionable" or "These premises are true, but they do not establish the conclusion with inductive force." In the real world of argument, however, people do make these sorts of assertions:

> "If you accept that humans have a moral obligation to reduce animal suffering, then you probably would become a vegetarian. But in fact we only have moral obligations to other people, not to animals." (The argument is valid but unsound since one premise is untrue.)

"The argument that we should extract resources like oil as quickly as possible and in as great a volume as possible assumes that these resources are infinite, but that's obviously not the case." (An unstated assumption is false.)

"It may be true that biodiversity is diminishing, but that does not mean that we should try to save every single species" (The premise is true, but the conclusion does not follow necessarily or probably.)

What this look at deduction and induction can give us then is a set of habits of thought, a way of thinking about arguments. And that way of thinking can be of use both in creating arguments and in evaluating arguments.

TO MAKE A STRONG ARGUMENT, DO THE FOLLOWING:

1. Clearly and force fully state your central assertion, the argumentative conclusion you want your reader to accept.

   Imagine that your reader is open-minded but tends to disagree with you, and pitch your argument for that reader. There is little point in presenting an argument for readers who already agree with you, though many people do exactly that. Don't worry about readers who strongly disagree with you and whose views are fixed; those readers probably can't be swayed. Instead, argue to and for the reader who is skeptical about your position but willing to change his or her mind.

2. Present your reasons in a logical order and show the reader how they necessarily or probably lead to the conclusion.

   The language of argument is the language of logical relationships: *since, because, therefore, then, it follows that* and similar phrases. The more clearly and strongly you can tie your reasons to your conclusions, the stronger your argument.

3. Give enough reasons to establish the conclusion.

   How many reasons are enough? There's no hard and fast rule for determining how many are sufficient. In part, the number of reasons you give depends on the space you have in which to make your argument. Put yourself in the position of the skeptical reader.

How many reasons would he or she need to accept your conclusion?

4. Demonstrate the truth or acceptability of your reasons.

Sometimes you can do this with common sense or common knowledge. Much of the time, research and citing expert sources will be necessary.

5. Don't worry about your own assumptions *unless* one or more of them might easily be challenged.

If you make a logical assumption in your argument and that assumption might be attacked, spend some time defending it.

6. Show the weaknesses of the opposing argument.

Since any one argument is always a response to an opposing argument, go ahead and engage the counter-argument directly. (See the next section on evaluating an argument.) To the degree that you can show that the opposing view fails to make its case, your argument gains strength in comparison.

To evaluate an argument, do the following:

1. Identify the conclusion.

The central argumentative assertion may be clearly stated at the beginning of an argument, or it may come at the end. In some instances, it may be strongly implied rather than directly asserted. To identify the conclusion, ask yourself questions like these: "What does the argument want the reader to believe?" "What new or different view does the argument want the reader adopt?" "What does the author want the reader to take away from the entire argument?"

2. Evaluate the reasons.

When the reasons supplied are factual, check to see if they are true. If a reason expresses a universal ("All men are mortal"), look for counter-examples. A single counter-example is enough to disprove a universal. When the reasons are judgments, check to see if they are acceptable. If they aren't,

3. Evaluate the adequacy of the reasons.

    Some arguments might sound good at first, but a closer look shows that the reasons offered, while true or acceptable, are too few or selective to really establish the conclusion. Has the argument left out important factors that, if included, would change the conclusion? Does the argument ignore realities that would undermine the conclusion?

4. Supply and evaluate the unstated assumptions.

    No real-life argument states every logical step; all real-life arguments contain logical assumptions. Those assumptions may or may not be factually true or generally acceptable. Supply the assumptions, show how they are logically implied by the argument, and then check to see if they are factually true or generally acceptable.

5. Evaluate the logic.

    Arguments are usually combinations of deductive and inductive reasoning. When the argument presents deductive reasoning, see if the conclusion does logically and necessarily follow from the premises. When the argument presents inductive reasoning, see if the conclusion does probably follow from the premises, and evaluate how strong the probability is.

6. Consider counter-arguments.

     A strong argument takes into account and deals with real or possible counter-arguments. If the argument fails to do this, it may be weak.

3.   Ethos, Logos, and Pathos

In this section, we'll look at additional tools you can use to improve the strength and persuasive ability of your arguments. Let's begin by looking at the two paragraphs below and analyze which one is better and why. Both are openings of papers about a particular method of coal mining.

Paragraph 1

Mountaintop removal is amongst the most controversial topics in modern society. Mountaintop removal affects not only the mountain itself and the natural ecosystem which the mountain is home to, but it affects many humans which live near the mining sites. The rate at which mountaintop removal has increased since its beginnings in the early 1970's is ridiculous and almost unreal. Mountaintop removal is happening mostly in West Virginia, Tennessee, Kentucky and Virginia and particularly affects some of the most poverty stricken areas in the United States which are small towns that lie in the midst of the Appalachian Mountains. These small towns are home to people who live a very simple life. Poverty stricken areas are much different than big city living, for instance these people have their homes, families, land, and not much else. With mountaintop removal jeopardizing their whole life it is unseen why it must continue.

Paragraph 2

In the United States, coal power is one of our main sources of energy. It's cheap and easy to access and it will be used as a source of power for a very long time to come. However, as the population of the United States and the world has grown, it has been necessary for coal companies to remove the coal with increasing speed in order to keep up with the rising demand for power. This has led to a shift in the way coal is mined. Instead of underground coal mining where many of the large deposits have been able to be removed, the method now is to strip the surface of the mine site in order to access veins of coal that were too thin to be feasible for underground mining. This process is known infamously as mountaintop removal.

Based on what you see here, which of the two papers would you prefer to read? Why?

In order to heighten our awareness and improve our ability to name what makes a paper good and the dangers associated with poor writing, let's ask ourselves a few questions about the two introductory paragraphs.

Which author seems more fair-minded? In other words, which one seems more likely to be understanding of reasons for and against mountaintop removal? What sorts of language—which words and phrases—indicate the level of fairness of each writer? Which author seems more authoritative? In other words, which one seems more like he or she is writing from a place of expertise?

Which author is going to explain the whole situation for us with details and facts that will make the issue clear? Which facts are included in each paragraph? What are they being used to prove? Which ones are most helpful for our understanding at this point in the paper?

Which writer seems to care more about the topic of mountaintop removal? Which clues make you think so? How does this personal investment affect your experience in reading the introductory paragraph? How might it be used more effectively? Which paragraph makes you care more about the topic or see its relevance to you or your life?

ETHOS

The Greek root, *ethikos*, means "moral" or "showing moral character"

We tend to trust those with exemplary moral character, and we often assess an argument, to some extent, based on how trustworthy the writer is. You probably find the second author more trustworthy than the first, and here's why:

- The second author explains the context of coal mining— why we use coal, why our coal needs are increasing, and why surface mining is used; therefore the arguments seem more balanced, more fair, and less damning of coal mining in general.

- By acknowledging that coal is an important energy source in the United States and telling us why, it does not seem like this writer is going to propose idealistic solutions, such as illegalizing the use of coal for energy. Instead, the reader gets the impression that this author is going to present us with a fair assessment of the need for coal and why surface mining is preferable in some ways to underground coal mining.

- This author acknowledges the fact that the term "mountaintop removal" has negative connotations.

- This author uses precise language to describe the benefits of surface mining that shows a clear understanding of how it works: "the method now is to strip the surface of the mine site in order to access veins of coal that were too thin to be feasible for underground mining." While we can infer that surface mining will be more destructive to the land than underground mining, this author is helping us understand how efficiency is increased through surface mining. Efficiency is a value that most of us share and hold as a high priority.

Here are some factors that get in the way of a reader's trust in the first author, ways in which the first author is not making the best use of ethos:

- The first author begins the paragraph with a questionable claim. Is mountaintop removal "among the most controversial topics in modern society"? A reader probably hasn't heard it talked much about. For those of us who know little about the topic, we are handed this negative name for the mining method before we even know what the method actually entails. This move does not seem wholly fair.

- The first author uses extreme language that makes me question her objectivity: "ridiculous," and "unreal," are used to describe the method of mining. "Poverty stricken" is used to describe the people who are being most negatively impacted by the mining. Use of extreme language makes a reader feel like someone's agenda is being thrust on him or her. Most people want to feel like they are respected as readers to use information and data to make their own determinations. Instead of "poverty stricken," a better description might be "poor" or "those in the lowest income brackets," or "below the poverty line." While poverty is a descriptive word that is not saturated with judgment, adding "stricken" to the word creates an unnecessary element of drama—as if the state of being poor has been shot from the sky like lightning or has hit the residents as by a violent hand.

- This author makes some careless grammatical moves, which makes me wonder how much time and thought were put into refining his or her points. For instance in the following sentence, "Poverty stricken areas are much different than big city living," the two parts that are being compared are not in parallel form. "Poverty stricken areas" refers to location, and "big city living" refers to lifestyle. As readers, we question a writer's authority when these sorts of inconsistencies exist—even if we aren't consciously aware that there is a lack of parallel construction. The phrase could be rewritten like this: Poverty stricken areas are much different from big cities.

- Yet, that sentence's logic is not sound. The sentence assumes that big cities lack "poverty stricken" areas. There is poverty in every big city in this country. So, what is the author of paragraph one really trying to say? It is hard to discern his or her intended meaning, which impairs our trust in the writer.

By employing ethos effectively, a writer is able to gain the reader's trust. Ethos is one of three parts of the art of persuasion described by Aristotle. You can heighten trust in your readers by showing: fair-mindedness, accuracy, authority, and expertise.

Logos

This word is Greek for "logic" or "reason." We increase the credibility of our arguments when we present them in logical sequences, in which each point builds towards the next point.

- By explaining the context of surface mining, the second author offers a more logical sequence of information.

- She begins by showing us the significance of coal as an energy source, its abundance, accessibility, and inexpensiveness. This information is important in helping us understand the need for mining coal. It is logical to present information in the order that offers the clearest, most organized, understanding of the topic.

- The second author proceeds to explain why the need for coal is increasing—population growth—and, therefore, why people are motivated to find more efficient ways to obtain the coal. Without this information, the reader may not understand why more environmentally damaging methods would be employed.

- In the second paragraph, we also obtain factual information that helps us understand the basics of the topic at hand. The description of how surface mining is done, "to strip the surface of the mine site in order to access veins of coal that were too thin to be feasible for underground mining," offers us a clear idea of the following facts: what this mining method accomplishes, how, and why.

Here are some ways in which the first paragraph is logically weak:

- As already mentioned, paragraph one's opening information is not factual or even necessarily credible.

- The reader already knows much of the information offered. We can infer that mining affects mountains, ecosystems, and people who live near the mining sites. Therefore, what does it accomplish, logically, to tell us these things? It would be more logical to tell us specific ways in which these entities are impacted by surface mining, and that information will be more meaningful to us after we find out what the method of mining entails, how it is done. The sequence of information is key to maximizing logic.

- Factual information that paragraph one offers is: mountaintop removal began in the 1970's, its use is increasing, it is most commonly employed in West Virginia, Tennessee, Kentucky and Virginia, and often in poor regions. Many basic details are not included, such as why this method is increasingly being used, what the method entails, and why it so often impacts poor regions.

Using logos helps your reader understand your subject clearly and thoroughly.

You can heighten understanding in for your readers by offering factual information in a sequence that makes logical sense.

PATHOS

In Greek, this word means "suffering"

While our goal is not to make our readers suffer, we do want to help them care about the topics we are addressing. In order to persuade someone of something—to see information in the way we want them to see it—we need to appeal to all of his or her decision-making faculties; therefore, we need to make him understand the issue cognitively and we need to engage him emotionally. While the author of paragraph one seems to care deeply about the topic of surface mining, how she presents her feelings on the topic can be problematic. In the second paragraph, the author does not tell us how she feels about the topic. Instead, she gives us information that can allow us, as readers, to care about the topic.

- Author two shows her readers how coal mining impacts us and why we should think about it. She does so by pointing out our dependence on coal as an energy source. This way we cannot say, "Oh, this subject does not apply to me."

- Next she shows us how our behavior impacts the increasing need for energy. Our decision to have children boosts our need for energy and motivates us to find faster, cheaper, easier ways to obtain energy—in this case, in the form of coal.

- Finally, author two appeals to our feelings towards efficiency. We don't want to let coal go to waste so we devise ways to procure the smaller deposits. We don't want to spend more money to maintain our current energy usage (read: standard of living), so we can see the value of more efficient methods of mining.

Author one, on the other hand, cares so much about the topic of surface mining that her feelings infringe on the reader's ability to engage emotionally with the topic.

- As mentioned earlier, much of the language author one uses is overstated or dramatic. Not only does this tend to cause the reader to question the writer's credibility, it also can feel overbearing. Words like "ridiculous," and "unreal" seem like they are trying too hard to make us care. Readers don't want someone to try to make them care. They want her to inspire them to care, to show them how they have a stake in the issue.

- We already discussed the phrase, "poverty stricken," and this phrase applies here, too. In an attempt to make us care about the poor who are affected by surface mining, the author risks sounding manipulative. Another part of paragraph one that seems potentially manipulative is: "These small towns are home to people who live a very simple life." The word "home" is an emotionally loaded word. It seems it is being used to evoke empathy. Most readers would prefer to learn more factual information about the people who are being negatively impacted by surface mining. Factual context can allow us the opportunity to care due to an authentic understanding of the circumstances in which poor people in coal-bearing regions live and how these circumstances might guide decisions about mining methods.

- The author of paragraph one spends too much time telling the reader how she feels and therefore implying how the reader should feel. It would better to describe the situation and its details so that the reader can naturally experience a range of feelings about the topic. This goes back to the adage, "Show, don't tell." We want to present the reader with a clear picture of the situation so he or she can see for him or herself how important a change in policy or behavior is.

You can help inspire readers to care about your topic by showing them how they are impacted by the situation, how they impact it, and what they can do to improve it.

Chapter 7. DOING RESEARCH

Chapter 7, Section 1 provided courtesy of Reference Librarian Megan Tomeo of Arthur Lakes Library at CSM.

Libraries collect, organize, and make available information in all subjects. Information comes in a variety of packages, including books, journals, maps, and digital data. Databases, library catalogs, and other tools provide ways for you to discover what information is available at our library as well as other libraries. A library is a collection, a space, and a tool that you can use to your benefit.

Learning to use a library and its resources can give you a competitive advantage as a student, and, once you graduate, as a scientist or engineer. This guide will introduce you to the basics of using a library. The skills you learn are easily transferred to other libraries and other resources.

The amount of information available is quite expansive. Do not hesitate to ask for assistance as you try to find information. Librarians are experts in recommending databases or appropriate tools, finding obscure publications, searching research tools, etc.

1. LIBRARY SEARCHES

DEFINING WHAT YOU NEED FOR YOUR ASSIGNMENT

Your assignment and your professor's requirements will define the type of sources you will pursue—books, journal articles, websites, etc. What type of sources you need determines where you will search for information (i.e., the tools you will use).

For example, if a professor asks you to write a short paper about what happened in Colorado politics last month, you need information from last month's newspapers, not books, and you would look in an index to find relevant journal articles. If you are asked to write a historical summary of Colorado's government, the information in books about the history of Colorado and the West will be more useful than that in newspaper articles, and you would look in the library's catalog. To start you on your path, determine your assignment criteria.

- Do you need the most recent information available, or will older information serve just as well? Different disciplines place different values on the timeliness of information.

- Do you need information written for the expert or for the beginner?

- Do you need highly technical or basic information?

- Do you need to cover the topic in-depth or just the highlights?

- Is your topic focused in one or several disciplines?

TYPES OF INFORMATION

Books generally provide a broad overview or a synthesis of the established knowledge of a subject. While books are excellent resources for students needing a general treatment of a topic, the extended publication process (usually a year from the time the author submits the work to the publisher) means that their information is not as recent as that in journals. Books can be scholarly or non-scholarly and in print or electronic.

Specific information, such as formulas or numerical values, will be found in a particular type of book—handbooks in this example. Encyclopedias, dictionaries, and textbooks are useful for general subjects, definitions, or concepts.

Journals contain short, focused articles, usually on very specific topics, and are the means by which scholars communicate the results of their research. Journal articles are generally published more quickly than books, so the information in them is more recent. Journals can be scholarly or non-scholarly. Scholarly journals will often have a peer-review process i.e., a group of experts in the subject vet the articles to determine if they are worthy of publication. Journals will be in multiple formats including print, electronic, or microform.

The **Web** includes a wide variety of information which is great in many situations, but not for everything. The strength of the Web is its ability to provide current news (including weather, politics, conflicts, or crime), recreation (sports, entertainment, movies, music, etc.), and information on special interest topics (hobbies, fringe social movements, or specialized areas of research). The Web can also connect you to people, whether it is through social networking sites or finding people's or business' phone numbers or addresses.

However, the Web is not always a stable publishing environment as pages can disappear. It gives the impression that everything is free, which clearly is not the case considering copyright and the proliferation of commercial resources. The ability to prove authoritativeness and accuracy is often hampered by unsigned and undated information. Like any type of information, the Web has inaccuracies and at times just plain wrong information.

WHERE TO ACCESS THE TOOLS AT THE ARTHUR LAKES LIBRARY

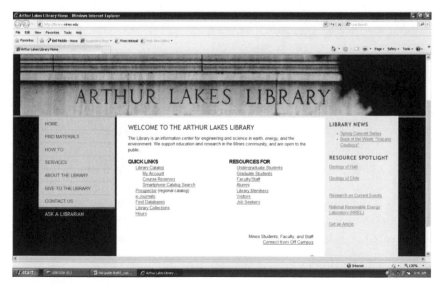

The **library catalog** has information about what items (books, government publications, journals, etc.) the library has available in print or electronic form and where to locate them . A catalog may be for one library, such as the Arthur Lakes Library Catalog, or a catalog could have items from multiple libraries, such as Prospector, the regional catalog in Colorado and Wyoming.

The Colorado School of Mines, by its degree offerings and its mission, is heavily rooted in applied sciences and engineering. The Arthur Lakes Library's collection reflects this emphasis. There will be certain subjects that our collection will cover better than others. A resource such as Prospector is useful for filling in other subjects.

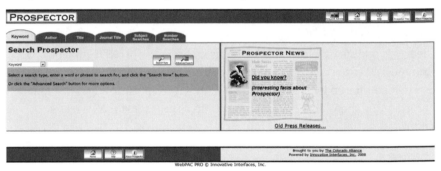

The **e-Journal finder** has information about online journals, including access dates. When searching for an electronic journal, use the journal title.

Databases help you to identify the journal articles, books, and other publications you may need. Databases can focus on content within specific disciplines e.g., GeoRef covers the geosciences, or they may cross multiple disciplines e.g., Academic Search Premier. Selecting a database which covers the topic you are searching is important. To determine if a database will fill your information need, consider the date, subject, format (i.e., are patents, articles, books, or conference proceedings included?), language, geographic limitations (i.e., are publications from only the United States?), and scope (i.e., are all specific journals indexed?). Information about the database is typically found within its Help guides.

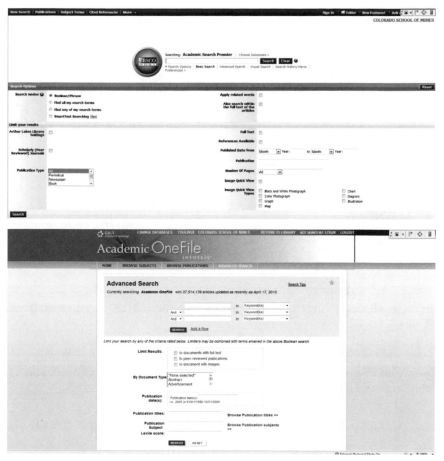

If you need help selecting a database, see "Research by Subject" (http://library.mines.edu/Research_by_Subject), ask your professor, or ask a librarian. The librarians have created help guides for courses such as NHV with links to resources and advice for students. These guides will help you identify the best tools for your research, how to evaluate information, and how to cite your sources.

Librarians are here to help with your research. Come to the library, call, or e-mail with your questions. Librarians' contact information is on the Library's website.

Search engines are plentiful on the Web. In addition to web pages, they will often search journals and books. Use caution: one search engine only indexes a percentage of the Web.

How to Search for Information

Searching for information that you need, regardless of what you need it for, can be a messy process. Browsing—strolling through the shelves or thumbing through a journal—is one way to search, but it is not efficient. The most efficient way to search for information is to follow a search strategy. Search strategies can be divided into three categories:

- Searching for a known item
- Searching for any works by a known author
- Searching for information on a subject

Searching for a known item. When you are searching for a known item, you are fairly sure that the item exists. Maybe you've found only an abstract of an article or you've used another writer's bibliography and have the citation information for the reading. You either need to confirm its existence or need to know if our library (or any other) has it.

1. Select key characteristics that identify the item. What type of publication is it—book or journal? How can you tell whether it is a book or a journal? Citations for books include publisher information i.e., publisher name and place of publication. Citations for journal articles include volume, page numbers, and journal title. If you cannot identify a publication, ask your professor or ask a librarian.

2. Select the tool to identify where the item is and in what format. When looking for an item at our library, the Library Catalog will be your first choice. There are other tools available, see "Where will you search for information i.e., tools."

3. Use the tool to find the item. When trying to locate an item, the title of the item is often used for the search. For example,

a. When looking for an article, search for journal title such as Materials Science Forum in the following citation.

Prasertsook, Somsak. 2009. Research and development of non-ferrous melting energy. *Materials Science Forum* v. 618-619, p.547-549.

b. When looking for a book, search for The Civil Engineering Handbook in the following citation.

Delleur, Jacques W. Hydraulic Structures. In The Civil Engineering Handbook eds. W.F. Chen and J.Y. Richard Liew. New York: CRC Press, 2003. p.37-1-37-44.

When you cannot find a known item, check that the information you have on the item is accurate (spelling, title, date, etc.), confirm that the tool you used is appropriate, or ask a librarian to help you locate the item.

Searching for any works by a known author. As you become more knowledgeable about your discipline, you will start to recognize authors who publish on particular topics within the discipline.

1. Identify the terms you will use from the author's name. The last name is the most important. For example, if you search for Stephen

Jay Gould's works using the term "Gould," your search will find all these forms of his name:

  a. Stephen Jay Gould

  b. Stephen J. Gould

  c. Stephen Gould

  d. S. J. Gould

  e. S. Gould

2. You will ALSO get all other "Goulds" in the database, however. Listings for first and middle names can vary, so if possible use them only to narrow down your "last name" search.

3. Select an appropriate database as your tool. If your author writes on a specific subject (geology, economics, etc.), select a database that covers that subject, as well as using more general databases.

4. Perform a name (author) search in a database.

When you cannot find works by a known author, check the spelling of the author's last name (and any other names you may have searched), confirm that the database you used is appropriate, or ask a librarian for suggestions.

Searching for information on a subject. Sometimes you know that you need information about a particular subject, such as wilderness areas or the energy crisis, but you do not know any specific authors or books that cover the subject. Fortunately, you can perform a subject search in library catalogs and databases.

You need to be aware, however, that there is no "right answer" in a subject search; you, and only you, can determine if you have gathered enough information to successfully answer a question or to meet the needs of your assignment. You may need to repeat some steps several times before you are satisfied with your results.

1. Define your subject need (What do you want?). Make sure you understand what is required in your assignment. If you have a choice of subject, pick one that interests you (it is much easier that

way). If you need ideas, consult an encyclopedia, your professor, or a librarian.

2. Define your scope (How much do you want?). If your subject is too broad (i.e., pollution), you will get too much information. If your subject is too narrow (i.e., the effects of pollution from abandoned gold mines on drinking water in Golden, Colorado), you won't get enough information for a good paper.

3. What types of information are required? Are you allowed to use web resources?

4. How much time do you have? Do you have time to get materials through interlibrary loan, or are you going to have to use materials in this library? (You may need to revise your subject if you do not have enough time.)

5. What keywords cover your subject? If necessary, use this list to broaden or narrow your results as you search. For example:

> a. The keyword pollution is too broad. It can be narrowed, such as water pollution, pollution from mines or mining, pollution effect on human health, or pollution in Colorado.

> b. The keywords "cancer from drinking water being contaminated from mine waste in Golden, Colorado" are too narrow. It can be broadened to cancer in Colorado, cancer from contaminated drinking water, or cancer associated with mine waste.

6. Select an appropriate database as your tool. Pay attention to the database's subject coverage—some databases are much better than others for specific subjects.

7. Perform a keyword search in a database.

8. Compile a list of items of interest (note any new keywords that you might want to use to search later).

9. Locate your items in the library or online. If you need assistance locating an item, ask a librarian.

10. Evaluate the items you have found (see "Evaluating Information"). Do they meet your needs?

11. If you need more information, or if you add to or change your topic while doing your assignment: Go back to the databases and refine your search or add/change keywords or ask a librarian for suggestions on getting more information.

12. Keep a record of the items you use for your assignment. Your documentation will be used for citations and a bibliography (see "Citations and Bibliographies"). Many search tools allow you to export or e-mail your search results—this is a very efficient way to keep records.

When you cannot find information on a subject, change your keywords (suggestions can be obtained from encyclopedias, thesauri, your professor, or a librarian), ask for help from your professor or a librarian to refine your search strategy, or ask a librarian for advice on using a database or which database to use.

EVALUATING INFORMATION

Just because something appears in print or on a web page does not mean that it is right or that you should use it. Information may be biased, out-of-date, or simply inaccurate. Even if it is reliable, it may be irrelevant to your needs. You must evaluate information sources and make critical judgments about their reliability and usefulness. This applies especially to information found on the Internet.

Similar characteristics can be used to judge a book, journal article, web page, etc. Regardless of the format, you should be able to determine the usefulness, authority, credibility, and scholarliness of the information.

Information is useful if it fits the criteria of your assignment.

- What is the length of your paper? Three to five pages? Then journal articles or book chapters may be more helpful. Writing a thesis? You may need the contents of entire book, journal volumes, conference proceedings, etc.

- How long do you have to write your paper? Two days? Then concise journal articles and not books may be more helpful.

- Are there any date restrictions? Either stated by your professor or implied by your discipline (e.g., geology often requires information from decades ago whereas physics typically requires only the past year or two). Be very careful of information with no publication date. Decide whether the information's age affects your need. Some information is useful no matter how old it is (like geologic strata descriptions or chemical formulas). Other information can be useless or even dangerous if too old (like medical procedures or engineering standards).

- Are you required to use only scholarly sources? See section on scholarliness.

- Is the information technical or non-technical enough to fit your topic?

Is the work authoritative? What are the author's qualifications or credentials? Does the author have advanced degrees in the subject matter, affiliations, etc.? If you recognize an author's name (for example, Stephen J. Gould), it may help you to evaluate his or her publications. When you develop a subject specialty you will learn to recognize the major authors in your field. For now, though, take extra care in evaluating the work when:

- There is no author listed.

- The author is also the publisher.

- The author has a well-known or obvious bias.

Who published the information? The publisher edits, provides financial support for, and distributes a work. Most of the books and journals we see are published by well-established, reputable companies, professional societies, or organizations. Many internet resources are not "published," but they may be sponsored by an organization, government agency, or university. Because publishers review the works published under their names, you can use the publisher as a guide to quality. Take extra care in evaluating the work when:

- There is no publisher or sponsor listed.

- The publisher is also the author (or the item is published on a personal web page).

- The publisher is an organization with a well-known bias (political party, etc.).

How credible is the information?

- Does the author state his or her bias?

- Does the publisher have a bias?

- Are there citations or references to other credible sources?

- Do other credible sources cite this work?

- Who is the intended audience?

- From what assumptions, judgments, and inferences does the author proceed?

Can the information be proven true and accurate through scientific inquiry?

- Are the author's facts and observations verifiable?

- Do the author's statistics, charts, graphs, and other graphics provide all the information necessary for understanding and interpretation?

- Do any polls or surveys performed or sources utilized have the ability to stand scrutiny on their own?

- What type of arguments does the author use -- emotional, factual, political, scientific?

- Do the author's arguments, data, and stated facts support his or her conclusions?

If a journal article or another work has undergone the scrutiny of peers and the rigors of academia, it is typically considered a scholarly work. If your instructor asks for college-level (authoritative and scholarly) sources for your paper, the source should have some of these characteristics:

- The author or authors are listed and credentials included.

- A bibliography or list of works cited is provided.

- There is an appearance of impartiality; there are no advertisements or unsupported opinions.

- The results of research, experimentation, or observation rely on reputable methods.

- It has been peer-reviewed i.e., examined and approved by a panel of experts in the field.

College-level sources include the following:

- Scholarly journal articles and books.

- Government publications e.g., Congressional hearings, research reports, regulatory information.

- Authoritative organizations e.g., Colorado School of Mines, American Society of Civil Engineers.

These sources are not college-level but still may be useful depending upon your assignment:

- News articles.

- Editorials, even if they're in a scholarly journal.

- Educational materials aimed at beginners e.g., K-12 web sites, text books.

- Encyclopedias, including Wikipedia.

Why do professors ask for college-level information? Because at the college-level, you are expected to dig deeper, consult cited publications, etc., rather than rely solely on non-scholarly works.

Citations and Bibliographies

Scientific, technical, and academic writing commonly includes citations and a bibliography, and you will be asked by your professors to do so as well. This is a critical part of your work for these reasons:

- Plagiarism and copyright violations incur serious consequences.

- Citing sources is the hallmark of scholarly communication. It provides the evidence on which you have based statements, arguments and conclusions in your research.

- By citing others you give them the credit they deserve for their intellectual property.

- You give your readers the ability to explore your ideas by providing them with related citations.

- Citing other works encourages you to think. By getting down on paper how others' ideas connect to yours, and by putting some of those ideas into your own words, you get the concepts more firmly into your head. Anything else is cheating yourself on your education.

Citations and a bibliography are used in conjunction to provide information to the reader about the sources you used in writing a paper or completing a project. (Footnotes serve a similar purpose, but are not commonly used in scientific and technical writing.) Citations are within the text of your paper and should be included when you quote (use exactly the same words) directly from the source, use information (facts, observations, ideas, opinions, etc.) from the source that you have restated in your own words, or reproduce pictures, graphs, or electronic files from the source.

Failure to acknowledge your sources is plagiarism. It amounts to claiming others' work as your own, even if you do it unintentionally. The academic and scientific communities treat plagiarism very seriously; plagiarism has resulted in formal apologies, suspensions, and lawsuits. When in doubt about what you need to cite, ask a librarian or your professor.

Most of your evidence needed for the support of your thesis would come from your own creative analyses of certain texts and from your secondary sources. Thus, you need to find reliable sources such as books and studies, journal articles, book chapters, and websites. This section teaches you to find reputable sources by asking the right questions about your sources.

Answer the following questions before you start your research.

- What kind of information are you looking for? Research studies? Facts? Opinions? News reports? Analyses? Personal reflections? History?

- Where would be a likely place to look?

- Which sources are likely to be most useful to you? Libraries? Academic periodicals? Newspapers? Government records?

If, for example, you are searching for information on some current event, a reliable newspaper like *The New York Times* will be a useful source. Are you searching for statistics on some aspect of the U.S. population? Then, start with documents such as United States census reports. Do you want some scholarly sources on wind power or genetic engineering? If so, academic journals, books, and book chapters are likely to have what you are looking for. Do you want to know about commercial products? Will those companies have websites with information? Are you searching for local history? Then a county library, government office, or local newspaper archive is likely to be the most useful.

2.   EVALUATING A BIBLIOGRAPHIC CITATION

Before you read a source or spend time hunting for it, begin by looking at the following information in the citation to evaluate whether it is worth finding or reading:

AUTHOR

To consider how reputable the author is, ask yourself the following questions:

- What is the author's educational background? Does the author hold a PhD?

- What has the author written in the past about this topic?

- Why or how is this author considered an expert?

- Did a teacher or librarian or some other person who is knowledgeable about the topic mention this person? Did you see the name listed in other sources?

When someone is an authority, you may find other references to this person. That is not a guarantee that the person is reputable, but it does indicate a reason to think the person is worth reading.

You can check the internet or the Library of Congress to see what else the person has written, and *Book Review Index* and *Book Review Digest* may lead you to reviews of other books by this person. There may also be information in the publication such as previous writings, awards, and notes about the author. Your goal is to get some sense of who this person is and why it is worth reading what this person wrote.

INSTITUTION

- What organization, institution, or company is the person associated with?
- What are the goals of the institution or organization?
- Does it monitor what is published? How rigorous is that review process?
- Might this group be biased in some way? That is, are they trying to sell you something or convince you to accept their view? Do they do disinterested research?

TIMELINES

- When was the source published?
- Is that date current enough to be useful, or might this be out-dated material?
- Is the source a revision of an earlier version? If so, it is not only likely to be more current but also something that is valuable enough to revise. Check a library catalogue to see which the latest edition is.

PUBLISHER

- Who produced or published the material? Is the group recognized in the field as being an authority?
- Is the publisher likely to be an appropriate one for this kind of information? Or might the publisher or group have a particular bias on this topic?
- Is there any sort of review process or fact checking? (If a pharmaceutical company publishes data on a new drug it is developing, has there been outside review of the data?)

Make sure the publisher is reputable. For example, a university press (Cambridge University Press, University of Oxford Press) or a government agency is likely to be a reputable source that reviews what it publishes. That helps to ensure the quality control over the material.

AUDIENCE

- Can you tell from the title (and perhaps the publisher) who the intended audience is?

- Is there a point of view being promoted? Sometimes, sources of information are really infomercials promoting the cause or product or bias of a particular group.

- Might the material be too scholarly, too specialized, or too popular to be useful to you?

3.   EVALUATING CONTENT IN PRINT SOURCES

After you have asked yourself some questions about the citation and determined that it is worth your time to find and read the source, you can plunge in by doing the following to evaluate the material in the source as you read through it:

- Read the preface: What does the author want to accomplish?

- Browse through the table of contents and the index: They will give you an overview of the source. Is your topic covered in enough depth to be helpful? If you do not find your topic discussed, try searching for some synonyms in the index.

- Is there a list of references or other citations that look as if they will lead you to related material that would be good sources?

- Does the author have a works cited page and footnotes or endnotes that show that the topic has been extensively researched?

- Are you the intended audience? Consider the tone, style, level of information, and assumptions the author makes about the reader. Are they appropriate for your needs?

- Try to determine if the content of the source is fact, opinion, or propaganda.

- If you think the source is offering facts, are the sources for those facts clearly indicated?

- Do you think there is enough evidence offered? Is the coverage comprehensive?

- Is the language objective or emotional?

- Are there broad generalizations that overstate or oversimplify the matter?

- Does the author use a good mix of primary and secondary sources for information?

- If the source is opinion, does the author offer sound reasons for adopting that stance?

4.   MLA DOCUMENTATION STYLE

Many of the NHV instructors will ask that you cite your sources using the Modern Language Association (MLA) documentation system. MLA is the style of choice for many humanities disciplines. While you will most likely not be using MLA in your eventual fields of study, learning the conventions of a particular style is useful, not only in allowing your instructor to better understand your writing and research, but so that you learn the details involved in following style conventions. You will be looking for similar conventions in other styles—such as which order publication information needs to be listed, how to order citations, how to refer to authors, how to indicate dates you accessed the text versus the dates of publication, etc.

Here is a part of a researched paper using MLA documentation style followed by the "Works Cited" list of sources:

Although the arguments against infertility treatments proposed are reasonable, supporters of infertility treatments also assert arguments that are difficult to refute. The most important argument for pro-infertility treatment concerns the individuals who desire to have children. In the academic article, "Health-related quality of life in infertile couples receiving IVF or ICSI treatment," Rashidi explains the emotional issues infertile couples face such as "depression, anxiety, social isolation and sexual dysfunction" (Rashidi, et al). The author's last name is in parentheses; readers can find the source in the Works Cited under "Rashidi." There are no pages numbers in this source. This explains why infertile couples and individuals desire to acquire the treatments. Besides the emotional problems, individuals who obtain these treatments also have to face financial challenges because the cost for these treatments is very high. With the pain and financial crisis that these individuals are willing to face to get the treatments, it is adequate to allow individuals to acquire their desires. Bagness provides the argument to refute conservative thinkers' argument. She suggests that utilitarians would approve of infertility treatments because scarifying some embryo may "enhance the well-being of future embryos" because after experimenting, the techniques can be improved and the deaths of embryos can be reduced (70). The author is mentioned in the text, so only the page number is in parentheses.

In "Technology and Infertility: Assisted Reproduction and Modern Society," Linda Bickerstaff justifies that children conceived through infertility treatments would have the same life as natural born children. Tyler Madsen, an IVF-conceived baby, declares: "Some people may think that my conception makes me different or special from others. In fact, I'm like any other teenager with the same concerns, the same goals, and the same dreams. I think all kids are special and unique. It doesn't matter how they are conceived" (34). Enclose in-text citations in parentheses ( )—not brackets [ ]. Anne Bernstein, a clinical psychologist and a research associate at the Council on Contemporary Families, supports Madsen. Bernstein believes that infertility treatments would not have any negative effects on IVF-conceived children (Bickerstaff 34). Generally the author and page number are included in parentheses. Only a space separates the author from the page number—no punctuation. Being born different does not make a person different. He or she still has the same right of life and resources as other people. Infertility treatments will not only help infertile couples or individuals, but also help generate life to many individuals who might not exist without this technology.

Works Cited

Bagness, Carmel. *Genetics, the Fetus and Our Future*. Hale: Hochland, 1998. Print.

Bickerstaffs, Linda. *Technology and Infertility: Assisted Reproduction and Modern Society*. New York: Rosen, 2009. Print.

Hardin, Garrett. "The Tragedy of the Commmons." *Environmental Ethics: Readings in Theory and Application.* Ed. Louis Pojman. Florence: Wadsworth, 2005. 305-312. Print.

"Infertility Treatment Controversy." *Health News Digest*. Feb. 11, 2009.16 Nov. 2009 <http://www.healthnewsdigest.com/cgi-bin/artman/search.cgi>.

McDonald, Catherine. "The Ethics of I.V.F. -The right to reproduce." Burning Down the House Publications. 1988. 16 Nov. 2009 <http://web.aanet.com.au/cmcdonald/Articles/The Ethics of IVF.htm>.

Rashidi, Batool. et al. "Health-related quality of life in infertile couples receiving IVF or ICSI treatment." *BMC HealthService Research* 8 (2008): 186. 16 Nov. 2009 <http://www.nc<http://www.ncbi.nlm.nih.gov/pmc/articles/PMC2553790/>.

Some things to note about citing sources in MLA:

- List sources in alphabetical order by last name of the author, when available.

- Begin a citation with the title of the article when an author is not listed. For example, "Infertility Treatment

Controversy," above, is listed under "I" for the first letter in the title.

- Provide as much information from the following list as possible: author, title, publication information.

- Place a period at the end of each citation—either after the word "Print" for printed books, chapters, or essays in anthologies (as in Hardin's essay, which is found in a book edited by Pojman), or after the URL and the closing angle bracket ">" for sources found on the web..

- Angle brackets <> should go on each end of a URL. For example, here is a URL with angle brackets and a period at the end: <http://inside.mines.edu>.

- Begin the Works Cited list on a new page.

- Double-space the entire Works Cited page without additional spacing between entries or after the title of the document, Works Cited.

- Each entry in the Works Cited list is a hanging indent: the second and all other lines are indented from the left margin. All word processing programs can do hanging indents; refer to the help file.

- Do not use bold or quotes for the title, Works Cited.

Some things to note about in-text citations in MLA:

- Indicate each source within the text of your paper in parentheses, with the first part of the entry and a page number, when applicable. For instance, when referring to information from Catherine Bagness' book, *Genetics, the Fetus, and Our Future*, we would place her last name in parentheses, followed by the page number on which the quote or information is found. The fourth source on this list does not have an author or page numbers and would be indicated in an in-text citation like this: ("Infertility Treatment Controversy").

- Place one space between the last name (or article title—or whatever the first portion of the source's citation) and the page number, nothing else: (Bagness 34).

- Place the period or comma, depending on where the citation falls in the sentence, outside of the parentheses (Bagness 34).

SAMPLE REFERENCES

Book by one or more authors

Bagness, Carmel. *Genetics, the Fetus and Our Future*. Hale: Hochland, 1998. Print.

Author's Last Name, First Name. *Book Title*. Place of publication: Publisher, Date of Publication. Print or <url>.

> Notice the period after the author, the period after the book title, the italicized the book title, the colon between the place of publication and the publishing company's name, the comma after the publisher, and the period after the date. For print sources in this digital age we need to indicate such. All entries end with a period.

Essay or article in an edited anthology (collection of essays)

Hardin, Garrett. "The Tragedy of the Commons." *Environmental Ethics: Readings in Theory and Application*. Ed. Louis Pojman. Florence: Wadsworth, 2005. 305-312. Print.

Author's Last Name, First Name. "Title of Chapter." Editor, *Title of Anthology*. Place of publication: Publisher, Year of publication. Page numbers. Print or <url>.

> When there is more than one editor listed, use "Eds." rather than "Ed." Titles of essays and articles are always in quotes; titles of books are always italicized. The page numbers listed are inclusive—first page to last page.

Essay or article in a journal or other periodical

Boehm, Robert F. "Heat Engineering." *Developments in the Design of Thermal Systems* 16.6 (1997): 190-206. Print.

Author's Last Name, First Name. "Title of Article." *Title of Journal* Volume number.Issue number (Date): Page numbers. Print or <url>.

> Titles of journals and periodicals are italicized. List the volume number and the issue number. The date appears in parentheses, and a colon introduces page numbers.

Essay or article in an online periodical

"Infertility Treatment Controversy." *Health News Digest.* Feb. 11, 2009. Web. 16 Nov. 2009. <http://www.healthnewsdigest.com/news/Family_Health_210/I nfertility_Treatment_Controversy.shtml>.

"Title of Article." Title of Periodical. Date of Publication. Medium. Date of Access. <url>.

> The citation begins with the article title since no author is given. The date the site was accessed is important to note since sometimes information on the internet changes or becomes unavailable.

McDonald, Catherine. "The Ethics of I.V.F. -The right to reproduce." Burning Down the House Publications. 1988. 16 Nov. 2009. <http://web.aanet.com.au/cmcdonald/Articles/The%20Ethics%20 of%20IVF.htm>.

> This online essay has an author.

Rashidi, Batool. et al. "Health-related quality of life in infertile couples receiving IVF or ICSI treatment." *BMC Health Service Research* 8 (2008). 16 Nov. 2009. <http://www.ncbi.nlm.nih.gov/pmc/articles/PMC2553790/>.

> An academic article found on a website: "et al" indicates that there were several authors, the number "8" indicates the volume number in which the article appeared

Williams, Joy. "The case against babies." *Granta* 55 (1996) 209-212. 16
Nov. 2009 *General OneFile*. Arthur Lakes Library, Colorado School
of Mines <http://find.galegroup.com>.

> An article found through a library database, which is called
> General OneFile; we need to give credit to the databases
> for the work they do, i.e. making articles available to their
> subscribers (Arthur Lakes Library subscribes to databases
> for our use).

5.   IEEE DOCUMENTATION STYLE

Many of the NHV Instructors will ask you to use the Institute of
Electrical and Electronic Engineers (IEEE) documentation system. What if
you aren't planning into going into electrical or electronic engineering?
Many engineering disciplines use systems very close to IEEE. Learning the
conventions of IEEE's system will help you become accustomed to
preparing research and data in a variety of technical fields.

Here is part of a researched paper using IEEE documentation style
and its "References" list of sources:

> In "The Tragedy of the Commons," Garret Hardin maintains that the
> population is growing exponentially and the resources of the Earth
> are limited. He claims, "The finite world can support only a finite
> population" [1, p. 306]. Label the first source you cite in your paper
> as "1." It will also be listed first in your References list. Indicate
> page numbers when they are available. Therefore, he suggests that
> the population growth must eventually become zero [1, p. 306].
> Separate your source number and page number(s) with a comma
> (or a colon). Hardin also upholds "freedom to breed is intolerable"
> [1: p. 309]. He explains that the more children in a family, the more
> difficult it will be for the parents to give adequate care to all the
> children. He also asserts that the public is concerned about such
> rights because the family with many children will consume all the
> available resources, which preclude others from their chance to
> utilize the resources. If everyone exercises the freedom to breed,

the population's growth would increase more drastically than it has. Hardin would disapprove of infertility treatments because the treatments would increase the population significantly, especially when these treatments can cause multiple births. Since the Earth is already overpopulated, the treatments would only contribute to the overpopulation issue. Many people, who believe global warming is actually happening, would assert that the increasing of population due to infertility treatments would only worsen the global warming dilemma because the more people occupying the Earth, the more resources will be used up and the more pollution and carbon dioxide will be released into the atmosphere.

Besides the overpopulation issue associated with infertility treatments come the problems of what arguments are appropriate to support these treatments. Catherine McDonald, an analytic philosopher whose interests vary, discusses the logic of the argument of "right to reproduce" those who support infertility treatments propose. In her article, "The Ethics of I.V.F. -The right to reproduce," McDonald declares that the "right to reproduce" is not a constitutional legal right because it is not indicated in the constitution. Reproducing is rather a matter of choice [2]. McDonald maintains that this argument is not coherent; hence, she refutes one of the reasons to support infertility treatments. McDonald believes it is more precise to argue that everyone has a right to the resources of society rather than the "right to reproduce" [2] Enclose in-text citations in brackets [ ]—not parentheses ( ). Designate sources without page numbers (such as websites) simply with their number. Every being has the right to utilize what society can offer; however, does that right apply equally to every human, or are there some people who are allowed to take more advantage of this right? What if infertility treatments provide a passage for some people to benefit from this right more than other people? The popular current situation of OctoMom, who is single, unemployed, currently gave birth to 8 IVF-conceived babies, and has 6 other IVF-conceived children at home, calls attention to this question. Some people might take advantage of the treatments in order to obtain child support allowances or such benefits while most of us are the ones who pay tax or does she love to have many children. Is it just for us?

REFERENCES

[1] G. Hardin, "The tragedy of the commons." In Louis Pojman, ed. *Environmental Ethics: Readings in Theory and Application*, pp. 305-312. Florence: Wadsworth, 2005.

[2] C. McDonald. "The ethics of I.V.F. -The right to reproduce." Burning Down the House Publications. 1988. [Online] Accessed Nov. 16, 2009.
http://web.aanet.com.au/cmcdonald/Articles/The%20Ethics%20of%20IVF.htm

Some things to note about citing sources in IEEE:

- List and number the sources in the order in which they are cited in the paper. For example, G. Hardin's "The Tragedy of the Commons" is the first source that this writer mentions. C. McDonald's "The Ethics of I.V.F.-The right to reproduce" is the second source mentioned in this paper, and so on.

- You may use the author's full name in your text, but in the References list, use only the initials of the first or first and middle name (G. Hardin).

- Provide the following information for each source in this order: Author, title, publication information.

- Single-space each individual citation and align each line of a citation.

- Double-space between each reference.

- List each source in your References list only once no matter how many times you cite it in your paper.

- Always refer to each source with the same number. For example, each time information from Hardin's essay is used, it will be cited as source [1].

- Each entry in the References list is a hanging indent: the second and all other lines are indented from the left margin. All word processing programs can do hanging indents; refer to the help file.

SAMPLE REFERENCES

Book by one or more authors

[1] C. Bagnes, *Genetics, the Fetus and Our Future*. Hale: Hochland, 1998.

[Reference number] Author name, *Title of Book*. Place of publication: Publisher, date.

> Note that the author is listed by his or her initial or initials. The title of the book is capitalized normally. If the book has more than one author, list all author by initial(s) and last name, commas separating each one.

Essay or article in an edited anthology (collection of essays)

[2] G. Hardin, "The tragedy of the commons." In L. Pojman, ed. *Environmental Ethics: Readings in Theory and Application*, pp. 305-312. Florence: Wadsworth, 2005.

[Reference number] Author name, "Title of essay." In Editor name, ed. *Title of Book*, page numbers. Place of publication: Publisher, date.

> In IEEE style, essay and article titles are treated like a sentence: only the first word is capitalized. If the anthology has a number of editors, list all be initial and last name, commas separating each, and replace "ed." with "eds."

Essay or article in a journal or other periodical

[3] R. Boehm, "Heat engineering." *Developments in the Design of Thermal Systems*, vol. 16, no. 6, pp. 190-206. June 1997.

[Reference Number] Author name, "Title of article." *Periodical Title*, volume number, issue number, pages. Date.

> Often scientific articles have a number of authors; you can list just the first author and add "et. al." ("et alia"—"and others").

Essay or article in an online periodical

[4]   C. McDonald, "The Ethics of I.V.F. -The right to reproduce."
Burning Down the House Publications. 1988. [Online] Accessed
Nov. 16, 2009.
http://web.aanet.com.au/cmcdonald/Articles/The%20Ethics%20
of%20IVF.htm

[Reference number] Author name, "Title of article. Publisher or
organization. Date. [Media] Accessed date. URL

Chapter 8. MAJOR PAPERS

Three major paper assignments are uniform across all sections of NHV. These papers will represent 700 of the total 1000 points a student may earn in the course of a semester. Instructors assign the remaining 300 points to assignments and activities of their choice—exercises, short papers, scaffolding exercises, attendance and participation, peer review sessions.

PAPER 1.   RESPONSE TO AN ARGUMENT

500-1250 words; 150 points.

In the first major paper, the student will summarize the argument presented in one of the course readings. The student should assume the reader is not familiar with the essay and should provide a clear and accurate summary for that reader using adequate paraphrases and carefully selected quotes.

In addition, the student will respond to the argument by agreeing, disagreeing, or agreeing somewhat and disagreeing somewhat. If the student agrees with the essay, he or she will present more reasons to support the central assertion. If the student is in disagreement with the essay, he or she will explain why its argument is weak and give reasons to support that position. If the student is in agreement with one part of the essay, he or she should give additional reasons to support it, and then the student should explain the weaknesses of that part of essay with which he or she disagrees and give reasons in support of his or her view.

The paper should meet these criteria:

1. Accurately and clearly summarize the argument contained in the reading.

2. Provide accurate paraphrases of the reading's main assertions that are the student's writing and not just modifications of sentences in the reading.

3. Quote selectively from the reading with proper use of author tags and correct MLA or IEEE citation.

4. State the student's position in agreement or disagreement (or partial agreement and disagreement) with the reading.

5. Clearly distinguish assertions made in the reading from the student's assertions.

6. Provide a coherent, logical argument for the student's view.

7. Summarize the reading and make an argument in clear, direct, natural, readable writing.

Sample Student Papers

Exploring "The Moral Instinct"

Bernard Beecher

Steven Pinker, in his essay, "The Moral Instinct", explores the reasons for human morality and the driving forces behind the similarities and differences in the moralities of different cultures, and provides evidence that these topics should continue to be explored. Pinker begins by tating that the universality of moral beliefs, and the argument that immoral people should be punished, defines morality. However, there is a recent moralization and amoralization of many ideas, with previously immoral actions becoming factors of human preference, and vice versa, when some harm has been associated with those actions. Pinker states that there is much hypocrisy in these newly defined immoral acts that finds its roots in specific lifestyles and the illusions of morality that fool the moral senses. Pinker supports this idea—that every human naturally possesses a "moral sense" linking moral actions to the brain and its genetic blueprints more profoundly than to environmental influences—with a range of examples and their implications. It is through this natural moral sense that people support their beliefs of wrong and right and judge the actions of themselves and others, even with no logical reasoning to rationalize their intuitions. Pinker agrees with the idea that there are a number of moral themes present in every human that span cultural lines, including harm, fairness, community, authority, and purity. He continues to explain that different moralities arise from different weight on these areas, caused by the genetics and environment of the person. Pinker also presents the idea that, despite critical beliefs that insights into human morality would reveal them as self-serving, the basic drive for self-replication of genes may actually lead to true selflessness, and the current mix of levels of selflessness provides the basis for society. This leads Pinker to explain the idea of moral realism: the presence of moral truths which will naturally be discovered and followed due to the existence of "non-zero sum games" and general rationality. Pinker concludes and restates his thesis by promoting the exploration of the moral sense as a tool to look past life's illusions to find the true morality behind an action, not simply as a means to breakdown morality itself.

Though some of the ideas Pinker suggests in this article could be considered somewhat controversial, the large amount of evidence he presents supporting his claims makes it simple to see the reasoning behind them, and I very much support them. He makes an attempt to connect all people, creating a common ground which might someday lead to better cooperation between cultures, as people may understand that the driving forces behind their beliefs are not so different. The idea that all morality is based on a few "moral spheres" and derived from a common natural "moral sense" is contrary to the ideas of many, who notice the many differences in morality among people around world, but Pinker counters these arguments by applying the idea of variable emphasis on the different spheres, and the idea that environment still influences a person's moral character, despite the strong correlation that has been discovered between morality and genetics. Pinker's main point in this essay, supporting the exploration of the science of the human sense, is very simple. He counters many arguments against delving more deeply into the basis behind moral actions, giving many cases where this exploration uncovers a generally more agreeable outlook on the human, such as the idea that genes that drive for self-replication may lead to an overall selfless being. It is understandable for people to retain some doubts, however, for there is no way to know if there is still an aspect of the moral sense that will change how we see morality in general, or how we see ourselves as a species. Overall, the thoroughness with which Pinker anticipates arguments of his critics, such as providing scientific evidence that toddlers have a sense of morality to counter views against the moral sense, as well as the manner in which he is able to make valuable connections and insights from scientific evidence regarding human morality and the moral sense, shows his skill as a writer, and provides a solid basis for a set of ideas which are difficult to denounce. [1]

Reference

[1] S. Pinker, "The Moral Instinct," nytimes.com, January 13, 2008. [Online]. Available: http://www.nytimes.com/2008/01/13/magazine/13Psychology-t.html?_r=1. [Accessed: February 3, 2010].

SUMMARY OF AND RESPONSE TO "MORAL DEVELOPMENT AND PROFESSIONAL ENGINEERING"

Corey Wible

The essay, "Moral Development and Professional Engineering," by Elizabeth Endy and P. Aarne Vesilind promotes the idea that there are stages that define a person's ethical and moral development and that being aware of them can help prepare one to make ethical decisions. They spur thoughts in the reader that contemplate the differences in people's responses to ethical predicaments. Proposing certain applications of the stages through hypothetical case studies encourages readers to consider their own actions in an ethical dilemma, so that they might be better prepared when they face a similar quandary.

Endy and Vesilind begin their article with the example of an engineer that is placed at a difficult impasse. The engineer is being forced to decide whether to submit results that the contractor who hired him or her doesn't want to hear or actually get paid for work the engineer did. The ethical standards that influence the engineer's final action are developed throughout his or her life. Engineers are obligated by society to acknowledge their responsibility to appreciate these ethical standards linked to their career.

Studies have been done that support the idea of quantification of the development of moral cognition. Endy and Vesilind highlight two studies with striking similarities between general moral development and ethical development within professional engineering. Moral development can be defined as the ability to recognize situations in which the response is based on goodness, rationalize a response, and complete said response.

Jean Piaget came to the conclusion that children move forward through definitive stages in their moral development and these stages can be quantified. Piaget performed his studies on children from the ages of 6 to 11, but later when Lawrence Kohlberg performed similar studies he extended the range of ages from adolescents to young adults. Kohlberg recognized six stages that reveal cognitive structures and which are moved through sequentially when a person experiences a new situation. When experiencing new situations, the person may develop new cognitive structures. Kohlberg's studies allowed him to organize six Piagetian stages into three levels.

Level 1, preconventional, consists of obedience and purposeful exchange where individuals are thinking only of their self interest. Level 2, conventional, involves having society-accepted motives and the idea that everyone should obey the law. Level 3, postconventional or principled, centers around the idea of majority rule, democracy, and identification of universal moral principles.

In addition to the stages of moral development, engineers go through ethical development in their careers. Richard McCuen determined that this professional ethical development was comprised of six stages. Endy and Vesilind base their presented stages off of McCuen's suggestions.

Level 1, or preprofessional, is based again on self benefit. Level 2, professional, states that the engineer is loyal to the firm and puts either the firm or profession above all else. Level 3, principled professional, is centered around human welfare, the rules of society, and universal conceptions of goodness.

Endy and Vesilind bring up three examples written to provoke readers into considering what they might do in specific situations, which then invites readers to identify the stages we are operating in. Case 1 is a situation of conflict of interest where an engineer must decide between helping society or staying loyal to the firm. The second case deals with loyalty to the engineering firm where an engineer is forced with a decision between ignoring other people's welfare or staying with the company. The third case concerns an unsafe design which is made by a rookie because her superior wasn't carrying out his supervisory duties. The superior doesn't acknowledge his mistake and leaves the rookie engineer to decide how to respond to the situation. In all cases, it appears that the higher level the engineer might act on, the worse the consequences for that engineer's career will be.

Vesilind and Endy conclude their article with the suggestion that no engineer can know exactly how he or she will respond to a certain situation unless he or she is put in it. The hope is, however, that their article raises some attention to and awareness of what the best actions might be. The authors will at least have the readers thinking about their possible responses in the future.

The argument Vesilind and Endy pose brings many concurring thoughts to mind, but I feel their assumption of the moral development is a touch unfair. They put the faith of the article into Piaget and Kohlberg's studies [1, p. 113], which I believe to be flawed. Although, whether you agree with the authors' faith in Piaget and Kohlberg's studies or not, their hope to bring attention to the various ethical dilemmas someone might encounter is an admirable one.

I agree with Vesilind and Endy's goal to make the reader realize the effect of actions in our moral and ethical lives: "In engineering, as in every aspect of life, the ultimate test of moral development is manifested in actions" [1, p. 120]. In bringing up the potential consequences for the example engineers [1, pp. 117-20], the reader gets a better sense for the realities of these ethical situations people are put into and are given the opportunity to consider what might be best for that situation.

Vesilind and Endy make the point, "Development from one stage to another occurs when the individual encounters an experience that does not fit into his or her present cognitive structures" [1, p. 114]. I believe that a person is able to move to the next stage simply by being brought up with certain morals, and without personally experiencing a situation that would have otherwise been the sole path to move to the next stage. The 'disclaimer' at the beginning of the article stating the numerically ordered levels is not to cause speculation that one side of the scale is better than the other; leaving judgment to the reader seems valid. It seems to me that the higher end of the scale, relying on universal moral principles [p. 115], will usually prove to be the better route if society as a whole is in mind, rather than professional success.

I find the statement made by Vesilind and Endy, "a professional engineer has, in addition to personal ethics, a second layer of ethics which apply to his or her professional conduct" [1, p. 115] to be a contradiction. Earlier in the article, the authors write: "The objective of this paper is to illustrate the parallels between moral development and the development of professional engineering ethics" [1, p. 112]. Because of the similarities between the development along with the stages of morals and professional engineering ethics, it is false to say an engineer has two sets of ethics. Rather, because the sets of personal and professional morals are nearly identical, they may in fact be the same.

Endy and Vesilind make strong points for the importance of bringing awareness to these different stages. The points on which I don't agree with them do not undermine the importance of the work they are doing in heightening engineers' understanding of considerations that need to be taken in making ethical decisions.. I am in agreement with Endy and Vesilind about the importance in people realizing what stage they might be acting from and what they can potentially do to better that situation in the future.

Reference

[1] E. M. Endy and P. A. Vesilind, "Moral Development and Professional Engineering,"from *Environmental Ethics for Engineers.* Chelsea, Michigan: Lewis, 1986.

PAPER 2.   RESPONSE TO A DEBATE

1250-1500 words; 200 points.

In the second major paper, the student responds to two or three readings that disagree on a debatable topic. The student accurately describes the disagreement for a reader unfamiliar with the readings and then enters into the debate. The student takes a stand on the issue, advances an argument in support of that stand, and criticizes the opposing argument. The student may advance a compromise position or a new point of view not yet represented in the debate.

The paper should meet these criteria:

1. Accurately and clearly summarize the opposed arguments.

2. Provide accurate and adequate paraphrases of the major assertions in the debate.

3. Quote selectively from the readings with proper use of author tags and correct MLA or IEEE citation.

4. State the student's position in agreement or disagreement (or partial agreement and disagreement) with the readings

5. Clearly distinguish assertions made in the readings from the student's assertions.

6. Provide a coherent, logical argument for the student's view and criticism of the opposing view(s).

7. Summarize the debate and make an argument in clear, direct, natural, readable writing.

SAMPLE STUDENT PAPERS

NON SEQUITUR

Joshua Johnson

Etiologically speaking, controversial views are held about the Challenger disaster. An incident in which the O-rings of a shuttle failed to seal completely, causing the shuttle to explode seventy-two seconds after launch. The cause of the disaster according to Roger Boisjoly as per his article "The Challenger Disaster: Moral Responsibility of the Working Engineer" was a result of poor management within NASA that overlooked his data and opinion as an engineer to approve the launch. The cause of the disaster according to Alan Gross and Arthur Walzar in their article "The Challenger Disaster and the Revival of Rhetoric in Organizational Life" was the inability of the engineers to effectively communicate the importance of the problem at hand. My argument will be opposing both authors in that I believe all managers should be placed in ethics classes because logically it follows to have the party lacking in ethics to be educated so as to prevent cases such as the Challenger Disaster.

Before viewing divergences in causation, let us first examine the events surrounding the challenger disaster. A majority of the information will be summarized from "The Challenger Disaster: Moral Responsibility and the Working Engineer" by Roger Boisjoly as it is widely accepted as an accurate recount. Several months prior to the launch date, Roger Boisjoly began to observe corrosion on the O-ring seals along different connection points. Boisjoly conducted small scale tests that demonstrated the affects of temperature on the O-rings. Following a shuttle landing inspection, Boisjoly found that the first seal and parts of the second seal had been corroded, which gave him reason to worry about the integrity of the O-ring seals. Boisjoly formed the Seal Task Team which was devoted to find a solution, however experienced trouble getting results as a result of lack of management support. Prior to the scheduled launch day Boisjoly and his team presented data to the management team in an attempt to explain why the shuttle should not launch at the expected temperatures for January 28th 1986. When shown pictures of O-ring corrosion in past missions the management team asked Boisjoly to quantify his results. Boisjoly explained he could not quantify his results and had been trying to acquire further tests on O-ring resiliency since October. The Managers discussed amongst themselves and came to the conclusion that Boisjoly's data was inconclusive and therefore the launch would continue as scheduled.

The solution proposed by Roger Boisjoly in "The Challenger Disaster: Moral Responsibility and the Working Engineer" mandates that engineers should behave morally and intervene in any ethically unsound procedures within their company that would otherwise lead to an unsafe product. Boisjoly has demonstrated his dedication by establishing ethics classes nationwide for the purpose of promoting moral behavior to eliminate situations similar to those that caused the Challenger disaster. Though Boisjoly had been "ignored, chastised before my colleagues and criticized for not getting approval of my design proposals prior to presenting them to NASA" (13) he places no amount of blame on a particular group or person. Boisjoly instead focuses on how the engineering community can make a change within itself to prevent incidents such as the Challenger disaster.

Alternate to Boisjoly's conclusion, "The Challenger Disaster and the Revival of Rhetoric in Organizational Life" by Alan Gross and Arthur Walzar takes the stance that quality rhetoric has near vanished from American life, the result of which is a lack of communication and ability to persuade. Essentially, the authors view the degradation of rhetoric in organizational life to be the ultimate cause of the Challenger Disaster. The authors state "the Challenger disaster argues for the need for contemporary organizations and contemporary scholars to take the art of rhetoric seriously both as a vehicle for deliberation and a perspective for analysis" (76). The engineers in charge of presenting the case of why not to launch were not effective enough in communicating to the managers why they thought the shuttle should not launch. The authors make a clear point that the managers report states the problem was a failure in the O-rings while the engineers report states the problem was a result of poor management decisions. Gross and Walzar compare the challenger disaster to a situation one human drives a force on another human such that it causes harm to the latter human. A physical study of such an occurrence would determine that the injured person's body was insufficient to bear the load of the force the injurer drives therefore causing a break or tear constituting the injury. In reality the injury is a result of the injurer's lack of judgment in the situation. Similarly, Gross and Walzar argue, the physical cause of the shuttle explosion was a failure in the O-rings to seal properly, but actually a result of the poor judgment of the managers at NASA. Gross and Walzar also point out that the managers operated on a different standard of judgment in which the Seal Task Team was unable to explain the importance of the seals in a manner comprehensible to the management.

Superficially, I agree with both papers seeing as the majority of their content is factual data and logical interpretations of the cause of the challenger disaster. I, however, cannot agree with either paper's etiology. Boisjoly concludes that engineers should learn to stand up for what is moral while Gross and Walzar conclude that engineers should learn better rhetoric, when really the necessity for more ethical, if not more intelligent, managers is an obvious priority. Classes such as Nature and Human Values are highly beneficial to the engineering community as it provides wisdom. However, teaching engineers morality does not solve the issue of having immoral or illogical management. Gross and Walzar elegantly explain that "Lund, Mulloy, and Reinartz should have thought and felt themselves inside Challenger with the astronauts who were in their care. It is from this perspective that the Challenger managers should have made their decision concerning the launch. From this perspective, we contend, they would not have failed to appreciate its ethical dimension; from this perspective, they would have found their own arguments entirely wanting" (85). Boisjoly's conclusion is true but not relevant to the problem at hand. Boisjoly says "you have a professional and moral responsibility to yourself and your fellow man to defend the truth and expose any questionable practice that may lead to an unsafe product" (14). Though Boisjoly's statement is true, it is a non sequitur in the context of solving issues similar to the Challenger disaster. It does not follow to provide ethical knowledge to those that already have a firm grasp of the "ethical dimension" (85).

On the same basis, I disagree with Gross and Walzar that the challenger disaster was "not a failure of understanding, but of agreement, a failure of the arguments of the engineers to persuade the managers," (80). The message Boisjoly was hammering into the thick skulls of Morton Thiokol and his ilk was clear and sound. The managers could have argued they made a logical decision based on the chart that showed the O-rings experienced problems at high temperatures as well as low temperatures, however, are dismissed from this excuse after Boisjoly shows them the photographs clearly indicating a difference between the problems at high temperatures and problems at low temperatures. Upon reviewing this, the managers reached a different conclusion than any of the O-ring experts; clearly an error. Gross and Walzar believe these contradicting results to be because "the Challenger managers were unable to understand the engineers; to its advocates, because of strong differentiation, they were duty-bound to ignore them. In neither case do the managers make mistakes in judgment; they simply judge by different Standards," (84). However, their reasoning is faulty; an incorrect decision that is viewed as correct by different but contextually irrelevant standards is still ultimately incorrect and does not justify the judgment made by the managers responsible for the Challenger disaster.

To elaborate on the non sequitur present in Gross and Walzar's argument, recall the metaphorical situation involving two individuals in which one is driving a force onto the other such that it causes an injury. Gross and Walzar accurately determined that the physical cause of the injured individuals body is a result of its inability to bear the driving force and the real cause is the poor judgment of the injurer. By Gross and Walzar's logic, the ultimate cause of the injured person's injury occurred because the individual, about to be harmed, was unable to communicate to the injurer his impending harm. However, if someone says "if you continue, I will come to harm" and the injurer continues either out of malevolence or an inability to understand why, then the injurer is typically punished for incompetence or malicious intent. Clearly, Boisjoly communicated his concern of the outcome should they launch below specific temperatures and gave supporting reasons. Since the Morton Thiokol management continued anyway and probably didn't act with intent to harm, their judgments can labeled as less than wise.

Conclusively, the just blame of the managers of NASA is apparent but the ultimate cause and therefore the actions taken to prevent such disasters in the future are misconstrued. I believe one man's ignorance cannot be solved by providing extra wisdom and knowledge to an already wise, or at least knowledgeable, individual. Managers and those in a position above those that are more knowledgeable on the product than the managers themselves should not be allowed to make technical decisions. Therefore I propose that all managers of engineers producing a product, directly or indirectly influencing the health of any other individual, be required to enroll in ethics classes. This would help instill a mindset into the managers that their main function is task delegation, and should not be pressing their own unqualified judgments into the decision making process. Ethics classes should continue to be given to engineers as a tool to empower them to overrule any poorly made decision on behalf of the managers

Works Cited

Gross, Alan. Walzer, Arthur. "The Challenger Disaster And The Revival Of Rhetoric In Organizational Life." *Argumentation* 11.1 (1997) 85-93.

Boisjoly, Roger. "The Challenger Disaster: Moral Responsibility and the Working Engineer." *Ethical Issues in Engineering*. Deborah Johnson. 1991. 6-14.

SYNTHESIS AND RESPONSE ON *WATER SCARCITY*

There is no life without water. It is by far the most important resource that we have on planet Earth, and yet little is being done to conserve water as our supplies of essential freshwater are quickly running out. There are a few out there that are trying to warn the rest of us about the current water crisis. Among these are Jon Gertner, a writer from *The New York Times* whose article "The Perfect Drought: The Future is Drying Up" gives an overview of the water crisis, Micheal Webber, whose article "Energy vs. Water: Solving Both Crisis Together" links the energy crisis and water crisis, and Sandra Postel, a freshwater ecologist, whose magazine article "A Water Ethic" discusses the environmental impact of water scarcity. Through different perspectives, these authors discuss the water market and its link to water scarcity, the larger problems produced by water scarcity, and some solutions to this crisis.

Each of these authors points out the broad issue of water scarcity, which is increasing demand and decreasing water supplies. While it is agreed that population increases have helped to increase demand for water, Webber points out that the growth of affluence also contributes to this increased demand, because people have more money to spend on things that consume both water and energy[2]. Both Gertner and Webber talk in depth about how supply is being decreased by the effects of global warming, demonstrating how higher temperatures would lead to less snow pack and higher evaporation rates[1,2]. Postel, while she agrees with the effects of climate change, also claims that the supply of water that we have will be even less in the future, as the development of a "water ethic" leads to water rights going to the in-stream ecosystems, making less freshwater available for consumption [3]. Though these authors approach it differently, it is evident that the market for water is indeed getting pinched.

In talking about water scarcity, both Gertner and Webber think it is essential that the energy crisis be simultaneously examined. These authors both draw a close parallel between the energy crisis and the water crisis, claiming that it takes water to produce energy and energy to produce water. Webber points out the vast amounts of water needed for cooling in power plants, as well as the greater need for energy to transport and treat water, calling it a "vicious cycle "[2]. Gertner echos this idea, pointing out how less water in water tables increases the need for energy to pump it out, and how greater needs for energy is leading to greater consumption of water, such as for watering corn for ethanol [1]. For the most part, however, both authors suggest that water and energy are closely linked and as the energy crisis gets worse, the water crisis will surely get worse along with it.

The lack of water is certainly having an adverse effect on the environment, as all of these authors are sure to mention. Webber discusses the environmental effects in terms of the energy used in getting water and its effect on global warming [2]. Gertner and Postel, on the other hand, focus on the freshwater ecosystems being harmed from the water being taken out of streams. Gertner mentions this only briefly, stating that environmentalist demand for water to be kept in-stream, but Postel makes this a main part of her discussion [1]. The in-stream ecosystems should have rights to the water as well, Postel asserts, and as an ethical society we should be making sure that "all people and living things [are] given access to enough water to secure their survival before some get more than enough" [3]. In one way or another, all of the authors make it clear that the water crisis affects not only our society, but the larger environment as well.

To help solve the water crisis, each of the authors mention that an adjustment to water prices should be made. Webber finds this to be especially important, claiming that it would make people aware of the problem and start to value water more. He sees this as a way to implement other solutions, and even suggests a water ration along with increased prices [2]. Gertner simply suggests that this tax should be in the form of a progressive tax, to prevent wasteful uses of water [1]. Though Postel also agrees with the importance of a tax on water, she still claims that it would not solve the real problem of ecosystem destruction, since others would just claim the right to that water [3]. Though the authors do not agree on the importance or implementation of a tax on water, they all see it as part of the solution.

Both Gertner and Webber discuss changing conservation habits. Gertner sees this as a big part of the solution, citing how the Southwest should use water practices that fit for their climate, such as water recycling and proper landscaping [1]. Using recycled water is also a solution proposed by Webber, who says that non-potable recycled water could at least be used in agriculture and for flushing toilets. Webber also suggests changing irrigation techniques to drip irrigation and changing cooling systems to air or hybrid air-water cooling systems[2]. By changing the habits of people and the systems we use, these two authors claim, we can reduce the amount of water that is consumed and help escape the water crisis.

To implement their solutions, Postel and Webber both propose federal government involvement, but for different reasons. Postel claims that the need to protect the natural freshwater ecosystems calls for the federal government to act for the common good. Postel asserts that this would be for the common good because we do not know the consequences of losing these ecosystems, and it would be better to "err on the side of protecting too much than too little of the remaining freshwater habitat" [3]. Webber, on the other hand, finds it important that the government integrate its energy and water policies, so that they realize the effect one has on another. Webber suggests that the Department of Interior or Commerce is given full oversight on water issues, instead of several departments sharing responsibilities, in order to ensure that water is being used efficiently [2]. Through these government programs, Postel and Webber hope to improve some of the current problems with water shortages.

I agree with most of the market and environmental concerns presented by these authors, but at the same time I find that the solutions that they present would be hard to implement. Both Gertner and Webber suggest ways that people could conserve water, but give very little detail how it they would get people to actually do these things. Higher prices and progressive taxes are some of the suggestions for helping people realize the importance of saving water, but even these prices modifications wouldn't have much of an effect unless the taxes were really large [1,2]. Since water is viewed as such an inelastic good, people would probably pay out higher amounts on water without changing their habits, telling themselves that they need the water. Also, at a moderate price increase it is unlikely that people would completely rearrange their habits of water usage because of the high start up cost of these solutions, such as the cost to re-landscape their property or to buy low-flow appliances. With a large spike in water prices, people may change their habits, but at great public turmoil. Still, this may be what needs to happen in order to see change in water consumption.

Also, I believe that Webber's idea of integrating public policy on water would be beneficial to society. If energy projects could see the effect that they are having on water and vice verse, we can come closer to breaking the "vicious cycle" that Webber mentioned and avoid meeting a "peak water" along with peak oil [2]. I also feel that water concerns should be paid more attention to in climate change efforts. Webber cites the example of the cap-and -trade system, which works well at reducing the release of carbon dioxide, but had "serious effects on water supplies that were not being considered" [2]. Because of issues such as this, I think Webber's integration policy would be a good thing because it would make sure that both the energy crisis and water crisis are being taken into account, so that a real solution to the problem can be reached.

Like Webber, I feel that the biggest thing that we can do is get people to value water. If people value water more, I believe that realistic solutions to our water crisis can be put into action, which would in turn help us out of our energy crisis as well. If we could all be aware of the true consequences of our wasteful water use, both to the water market and to the environment, our combined efforts to conserve water can bring us out of our current crisis.

References

[1] J. Gertner. "The Perfecct Drought: The Future is Drying Up" From *The New York Times*. October, 2007.

[2] M. Webber. "Energy versus Water:Solving Both Crisis Together" From *The Scientific American*. October, 2008.

[3] S. Postel. "The Missing Piece: A Water Ethic" From *The American Prospect*. June, 2008.

PAPER 3.   RESEARCHED ARGUMENT

1750-2500 words; 350 points.

The third major paper is a researched argument. The topic for the paper should meet these criteria:

- It has to have something to do with engineering issues.

- It has something to do with either engineering and ethics or engineering and the environment,

- It has to be genuinely controversial; there have to be reasonable, opposed views.

The topic may be a case study, an analysis of one particular, concrete, real engineering event or situation. The topic may also be a broader issue that can be treated adequately in the space allowed. Students may argue for one point of view within the debate; students may argue for a compromise position or a point of view not yet represented in the debate.

The paper should have a reasonable number (5-7) of sources, some of which may be purely factual, but some of which must be argumentative. Instructors may also want to specify a minimum number of sources that must be print. Instructors may also require that students include a source in engineering or environmental ethics.

The paper should meet these criteria:

1. Accurately and clearly summarize the debate for a reader unfamiliar with the topic.

2. Clearly state the student's position in relation to existing arguments.

3. Accurately and clearly explain relevant facts, drawing on and correctly documenting all material paraphrased from or quoted from sources.

4. Provide a coherent, logical argument for the student's position and criticism of the opposing view(s).

5. Clearly distinguish assertions drawn from sources from the student's assertions.

6. Quote selectively from sources and document quotes in correct MLA or IEEE form.

7. Summarize the debate and make an argument in clear, direct, natural, readable writing.

SAMPLE STUDENT PAPERS

TO SPRAY OR NOT TO SPRAY, THAT IS THE QUESTION: A NEGOTIATION ON THE USE OF AGRICULTURAL PESTICIDES

Kevin Fiorini

1.0 INTRODUCTION

While pesticides have been present since the beginning of domesticated agriculture, the modern use of pesticides develop until the beginning of World War II, when only 30 pesticides existed. Some of the first uses of modern pesticides include insect control in order to limit the mosquito populations causing malaria. Within the past several decades, the number of pesticides has grown significantly, such that there are currently

900 active chemical pesticides with 1.8 billion kilograms applied annually worldwide [1].

A pesticide "refers to any device, method, or chemical that kills plants or animals that compete for humanity's food supply or are otherwise undesirable" [1]. In addition, pesticides are usually perceived as being a synthetic chemical not found naturally within the environment.

The major benefits include better health by controlling disease vectors and better supply of food. For several years, many saw pesticides as a flawless cure to disease and world hunger.

However, in 1962, Rachel Carson's book Silent Spring began to cast doubts on the risks and negative side effects of using pesticides. With the publication and widespread popularity of the novel, the public began to question whether the benefits of pesticides outweighed the risks, leading to a debate between farmers, scientists, and politicians on both sides that remains to be resolved.

In exploring the arguments of both sides, this paper will attempt to inform the reader of both sides of the debate in addition to devising acceptable solutions to move the debate closer to resolution.

2.0 THE ARGUMENTS AGAINST AGRICULTURAL PESTICIDE USE

A majority of the arguments against the use of agricultural pesticides focus on the intrinsic value of both the human life and the natural environment. The main arguments of cost versus benefit focus on both direct and indirect cost in order to assess the full effect the application of pesticides have on the environment. The arguments center around environmental, social, economic, and political arguments. In addition, the ideal of farming without pesticides is realized through organic farming, which has set out to prove that synthetic chemicals are not needed for successful agriculture.

2.1 Environmental Arguments

The largest argument against the use of pesticides is the argument that pesticides exact a toll on the environment that do not justify their use.

According to this argument, the use of pesticide in the United States has led to serious environmental consequences in aquatic systems that are largely irreversible. Several large fisheries in North America have deteriorated due to ever-growing concentrations of both synthetic pesticides and fertilizers, including the region where the Mississippi River feeds into the Gulf of Mexico. Runoff of synthetic chemicals from the Corn Belt in North America polluted this region to such an extent that it is known as the "dead zone" due to the loss of its ability to support life [2]. Advocates against pesticides also point toward the runoff of synthetic chemicals into critical watersheds for groundwater which results in the gradual but devastating pollution of the largest source of water for Americans. With an inability to control the groundwater, pollution which reaches these water reserves spreads across state boundaries and holds the potential for endangerment of many human lives as well as threatening of agricultural and wildlife habitats depending on the groundwater.

This view point also highlights that on land, pesticides have similar devastating effects. In addition to killing pests, many pesticides have to potential to destroy natural predator and enemy populations that help control pests [3]. This leads to a booming of the pest population, prompting an increase in the amount of pesticides used. However, increasing the use of pesticides acts toward the pest benefit, naturally selecting resistant species until the pesticides become ineffective [3]. The positive feedback results in an unending cycle resulting in ever increasing costs and ever increasing risk of loss of a crop due to pests which have grown resistant to pesticides.

These values portray the view point that the environment is both instrumentally and intrinsically valuable. Because pesticides have the potential of destroying natural habitats, they limit the ability to use nature for recreational activities such as fishing where nature is instrumentally valuable and they limit the ability to preserve land in its natural condition, constricting the intrinsic value of nature. This loss of value in the environment resulted in many environmentalists joining the fight against pesticides in order to protect the value of the environment.

2.2 Social Arguments

It is estimated that approximately one million humans are poisoned by pesticides each year, with 20,000 of those poisonings resulting in deaths [3]. Many people against the use of pesticides point largely to the health risks posed by using synthetic chemicals. Acute toxicity is well documented through scientific experiments and through observing the effects of accidental ingestion [4]. Although information on chronic human illness resulting from exposure is not well known, including cancer, many feel that the animal studies which suggests dysfunction caused by exposure provide enough evidence to severely restrict and even banning pesticide use, arguing that no benefit is worth losing a human life.

2.3 Economic Arguments

Some argue that pesticides also carry many hidden costs. In an evaluation conducted on the costs of pesticides, it was determined that the direct cost was $4 billion, with a benefit of $16 billion in increased crop yield revenues. However, upon assessing the indirect costs, including those outlined in the environmental and social arguments, it was determined that pesticides had an indirect cost of at least $8 billion dollars. While the farmer only directly pays for approximately $3 billion of the costs, society must pay for the $3 billion in consumer costs as well as the additional $5 billion not included in the direct cost [3]. While the benefit still outweighs the costs, the steady increase in costs and decline in profit benefits holds the potential of leading to pesticides becoming unprofitable in the future.

2.4 Political Arguments

The major political argument holds that the use of pesticides is not regulated enough, and that the regulatory structure in place is inadequate. Of 600 pesticides registered in the United States, the National Residue Program has the ability to test for the presence of 41 [2]. The large gap in testing places concern for the true level of pesticides on foods that are unable to be tested. Of those that are tested, one to three percent of the foods contain residue levels above the legal tolerance level [3]. While the percentage is small, the danger of purchasing food with illegal levels of pesticides remains disconcerting to many people.

Recently in California, lawyers have begun to argue that the political system is also not doing enough to protect the farm workers. Of the documented pesticide violations, 85% carried no fine, which was seen as a disregard to human life. In addition, it was found that 77% of farm workers poisoned by pesticides were caused by spray drift or residues. California, the largest agricultural state in the United States, is being called upon to institute minimum penalties for violations in order to promote the safe use of pesticides and encourage the use of sustainable alternatives [4].

2.5 Benefits of Organic Farming

Those fighting against pesticides have pushed for the development and popularity of organic farming, the practice of not using synthetic chemicals while farming. In order to determine the benefits of organic farming, a 22-year study was conducted at the Rodale Institute FST in Kutztown, Pennsylvania comparing conventional, animal and legume based organic, and legume based organic. The experiment found, among other things, that organic farming resulted in higher levels of soil organic matter, which conserves soil and water resources and allows for better drought resistance [2]. Fossil energy requirements were also 30% lower, increasing the benefit to the environment [2]. One of the objects for the experiment and for the author of the paper was to prove that synthetic chemicals are not required for successful agriculture.

3.0 THE ARGUMENTS FOR AGRICULTURAL PESTICIDE USE

The arguments for the use of pesticides generally focus on the instrumental value of the land in consideration. These groups look at not just sustainable agriculture, but also focus on providing food for a growing world population. By emphasizing the demand, supporters of agricultural pesticide see justification in the use of pesticides as a means of supplying the demand. However, these groups also see the necessity of restraint. Two of the articles used in this section address this point, saying "to maximize the benefits of pesticide use at minimum human, environmental and economic cost, pesticides must be strictly regulated and used judiciously by properly trained and appropriately equipped personnel, ideally in tight integration with other complementary technologies" [6] and "Properly used pesticides provide benefits essential to our way of life" (emphasis added) [7]. Thus, while advocating the use of pesticides, these groups generally advocate the sustainable, regulated use of pesticides in order to maximize the benefits of using synthetic chemicals.

3.1 Economical Arguments

In the view of supporters, pesticides have produced large economic benefits. Herbicides, which account for half of all pesticides used for crop protection, help save $13 billion in farm income loss due to pests [6]. In addition, pesticides reduce the risk of catastrophic loss due pest and disease, stabilizing the agricultural market and delivering food security [6]. The increased food security also delivers financial security to the agricultural sector of the economy. Pesticides can also be applied upon storage in order to prolong the shelf life of different crops by preventing spoilage due to pest infection [6]. This increases the profit gained from crops due to the decrease in losses. The combination of all of these benefits results in less than 2% of the United States population working in the primary sector of providing food [7], allowing the large majority of the population to work in secondary and tertiary sectors to provide manufactured goods and services for domestic use and for trade.

3.2 Social Arguments

Countering the social argument of those against pesticide use, those favoring pesticide argue the presence of some pesticides is actually beneficial due to the idea of hormesis. Hormesis is the scientific theory that small amounts of toxins are actually beneficial for the immune system, until a certain level where the toxicity begins to have harmful effects. Based on their studies, supporters of pesticide use claim farmers, foresters, and millers, who come into most contact with pesticides, actually have much lower cancer rates than the average population [5]. In addition, the supporters point out that the Maximum Residue Levels (MRLs) set by the government are below hazardous levels, stating that MRLs are often not approved unless it is 100 times below the no observable adverse effects level [6]. The supporters also point out that plants produce their own pesticides, claiming that 60% of natural pesticides are carcinogens at the maximum tolerated dose in rodent tests and that the daily consumption of natural pesticides was 20,000 times higher than the daily consumption of synthetic pesticides.

In addition to health, pesticides provide several social benefits which often go unnoticed. The blemish free food found in most grocery stores, market places, and in processed food is due to the use of pesticide [7]. Pesticides also extend growing seasons of certain crops, allowing for longer periods of providing fresh products to local and global markets [5]. The large food selection in turn leads to better nutrition and better health, increasing productivity of the society [6]. In addition, with the help of pesticides, food production is able to be sustained in order to support the growing population [7].

3.3 Environmental Arguments

Despite the claims of some of the dissenters, the use of pesticides provides some benefits to the environment. By increasing the yield per acre, smaller amounts of land are needed to grow the same amount of food. Thus, less pressure is felt to develop uncultivated land for agriculture [6], allowing for the preservation of wildlife habitat [7]. Pesticides can also be used to control the introduction or spread of an exotic species threatening to overtake both agricultural and natural habitat lands [7]. Although the natural predators of the species were not brought over, an effective pesticide can act to control the population and prevent it from destroying the agricultural sector or the natural land.

4.0 COMPARISON AND COMMON GROUND

Aside from the use of disuse of pesticides, the two groups have other differences. The supporters of pesticide use look more toward growing crops in order to increase supply through careful regulation and oversight of pesticides. On the other hand, most dissenters of pesticide use feel the regulation and oversight have been largely ineffective and that even the controlled use of pesticides has caused too much damage to the environment for the benefit to outweigh the cost. The dissenters tend to favor organic farming, which bans the use of synthetic chemicals.

While the positive consequences have been mentioned on both sides and the argument address, little has been said about the negative consequences which exist on both sides. The dissenters point out the environmental affects and future affects of pesticides due to toxicity. However, the supporters of pesticides point toward the inability of organic farming to adequately control pests in every situation and the common struggle against plant pests and weeds that have the potential of overtaking a field when left untreated. Undoubtedly, each side has its weak points.

While both groups have their differences, several key commonalities arise. Both groups look to meet the food demand of the world population. For decades, it has been the goal to eliminate hunger, which is being pursued by both groups. Also, both sides desire to maintain a healthy, growing population, whether by limiting health risks caused by cancer from restraining from using pesticides or by achieving the same result by using pesticides to grow foods out of season. In addition, both groups desire to have a sustainable food production. Lastly, both groups are constantly looking to improve the quality of the agricultural practices.

5.0 SOLUTIONS

5.1 Solution through Research

One option open to solving the differences between the use of pesticides is the additional research of pesticide application and pesticide removal

Currently, most pesticides are applied through spray application, including land and aerial application. Over the years, the land and aerial applications have been improved, but a few problems remain. The largest is the drifting of pesticides away from the target crop. During aerial application, approximately 50-70% of the pesticides drift on to neighboring fields [3]. Also, speed sprayers and mist blowers tend to have 35% of the applied pesticide miss the target crop. This leads to the accidental overexposure to pesticides by farm workers, as expressed by the dissenters of pesticide use. The problems resulting from this include greater risk of pest resistance and the decrease in productivity caused by toxic effects of the pesticide on non-target crops.

By reducing the amount of pesticide drift through enhanced application methods, accidental exposure is significantly decreased. However, finding feasible alternative application methods remains a technical challenge. Hand application is possible, but time and labor intensive, greatly increasing the cost of using fertilizers. In addition, application by irrigation runs the risk of greatly increasing ground water and surface water contamination, which would cause greater dissent from those who disfavor pesticide use.

A method requiring little to know application of pesticides includes genetically modified organisms (GMOs). GMOs are engineered to allow for a specific pesticide to be used without damaging the plant or with the pesticide already in the gene pool. While GMO technology came out relatively recently, much controversy still lies in whether or not the foods are safe. Currently, GMOs are regulated under the same food laws as other products. Many European countries ban GMO foods from the market, but other countries are still debating, leading to the possibility of losing markets upon pursuing genetically modified food production [8].

Research could also be done in removing pesticide residues from products used for consumption. The process would include applying chemicals to the products such that a chemical reaction removes the pesticide residue, leaving only inert, non-toxic products that are safe for ingestion by humans or are easily washed off the product. This would satisfy the pesticide supporters in that they would be able to still use pesticides. However, those against pesticide use would only advocate this solution if no residues remained from the removal of the pesticide. In addition, objections about the increase in prices may lead to the discouragement of this solution.

While these methods of calling for more research are appealing, they do little to resolve the debate. Most favor the side of the pesticide supporters with very little for the pesticide dissenters, leading to a shift in the argument rather than a negotiation. If these solutions were to be put in place, additional steps would need to be taken in order to gain the approval of groups against pesticide use

5.2 Solution through Integration of Natural Processes

Natural processes include using environmental resources already present in order to decrease, or possibly eliminate, the need for pesticides

Increasing vegetation growth around fields is one way to decrease the need for pesticides. The increased vegetation decreases the runoff from the field, absorbing excess moisture and pesticides. Depending on the location of the field, tall enough vegetation, such as trees, can be planted to limit pesticide drift by acting as a wind block and acting as a wall to block the flow of pesticides from one field to another.

Another natural process to utilize is natural predators. The natural predators act as a control on the pest population without the pesticides, but some pesticides kill of the natural predators until little or no natural control remains for the pest. To actions can be taken to benefit from natural predators. The first is to decrease pesticide use. To fully make the solution work, however, education of the farmers on the introduction and management of natural predators would be needed. The second option is to develop pesticides that do not severely affect the natural predator population while remaining effective on the pest population. A significant amount of research would be required, but the application of this solution would increase support from both sides, leading to a possible negotiation between the two parties.

Additional natural process include adopting of organic technologies and practices in conventional agriculture as suggested by [2]. This includes using off-season crop cover, implementing more extended crop rotations, increasing level of soil organic matter, and employing natural biodiversity. These steps are already starting to be integrated into conventional agriculture. However, to increase the acceptance of the new practices, education of current and future farmers should take place in order to highlight the benefits of adopting these practices. The education will also allow for the farmers to learn how to optimize yields and profits while using these methods.

The integration of natural processes holds the highest feasibility for success and for integration into the agricultural system right now. Also through the integration, it provides both sides with an acceptable solution that increases environmental friendliness and sustainability while still allowing the use of pesticides for a minimized portion of pest control.

5.3 Solution through Policy

Two additional solutions call for a change in political policy. The first is a call for national or global scale policy change, and the second is for more regional and local policy change.

The first change in policy would ideally take effect globally, but is more feasible on the regional or national scale. The policy include using incentives to entice agriculture to occur in places most suitable for agriculture and using the less beneficial land for other uses. This would limit not just the pesticide use, but also fertilizer, irrigation, and electricity use, since areas that can support a high agriculture would need less of the listed activities in order to grow a profitable crop.

The second option is more local in scale. Rather than changing the current policy, the enforcement of the current policy would be increased. This includes the ability to monitor and test fields as needed, but not freely without constraint. Also, more local, decentralized governing bodies are given power to interpret, with constraint, the current policy such that it fits the local climate and area available for agriculture.

Similar to the additional research, the change in policy often ends up being medium to low in feasibility. The addition of watchdog organizations would lead to higher costs to the central government, which may lead to tax increases. In addition, incentives would need to be paid though increased taxes or by cutting other programs. Given the current state of the economy and the government, the feasibility of passing a policy with such economic implications is low. In addition, a stalemate is often occurs due to political polarization and a lack of popular concern for agricultural policy. These trends can be combated through education of the benefits of a change in policy and by finding ways to politically discharge the hot topics of concern.

References

[1] "Pesticide," BookRags.com [Online]. Available http://www.bookrags.com/research/pesticide-woi/. [Accessed 12 April 2010].

[2] D. Pimentel, et. al., "Environmental, Energetic, and Economic Comparisons of Organic and Conventional Farming Systems," *BioScience,* July 2005, v55, n7, p. 573-582. Acedemic OneFile (database on Gale system).

[3] D. Pimentel, et. al., "Environmental and economic costs of pesticide use," *BioScience*, Nov 1992, n10. Academic OneFile (database on Gale system).

[4] "California laws not protecting farmworkers from pesticides, activist group charges," *Pesticide & Toxic Chemical News*, Jul 1, 1999. Academic OneFile (database on Gale system).

[5] R. Carson and A. Trewavas, "The true price of progress," Chemistry and Industry, Jan 19, 2004. AcademicOne File (database on Gale system).

[6] J. Cooper and H. Dobson, " The benefits of pesticides to mankind and the environment." *ScienceDirect*, March 2007. Academic OneFile (database on Gale system).

[7] F Whitford, , et. al., "The Benefits of Pesticides: A Story Worth Telling," Purdue University. Academic OneFile (database on Gale system).

[8] R. D. Olson. "Hard Red Spring Wheat at a Genetic Crossroad: Rural Prosperity or Corporate Hegemony."

DISAPPEARING HONEYBEES: THE POTENTIAL AGRICULTURAL CRISIS

Zack Page-Belknap

Introduction

In November of 2006, a beekeeper named Dave Hackenberg made one of the most confounding discoveries of the decade. As usual one afternoon, Hackenberg proceeded to examine a portion of his approximately 3,000 beehives for health, and honey, only to find... nothing. Almost two-thirds of Hackenberg's honeybee hives were completely empty with no sign of death or reason for departure [1, p. 4]. Being the former president of the American Beekeeping Federation and a commercial beekeeper for almost half a century, Hackenberg knew this was not merely a coincidence and proceeded to inform the Department of Agriculture's Bee Research Center [2, p. 5]. This phenomenon, which has now been coined as Colony Collapse Disorder (CCD), holds the potential to cause detrimental damage to the agriculture of the United States, and possibly the world.

Background

Perhaps the most prevalent question on a non-expert's mind when asked about the disappearance of honeybees is: why should I care about what happens to the honeybee? All they do is sting and make a delicious golden addition to our tea and biscuits, right? Wrong. Honeybees are responsible for pollinating and developing a little more than a third of the United States' entire crop yield [2, p. 11]. Fruits, vegetables, and nuts including apples, almonds, blueberries, tomatoes, cucumbers, and pumpkins rely almost solely on the work done by honeybees, and without their pollination, the cost of maintaining the amount of crop yield needed to support the United States would rise exponentially [2, p. 23]. The United States Department of Agriculture has stated that every one in three bites of food eaten per meal is directly or indirectly credited to the support provided by honeybees [3]. If the honeybees perish, not only would a heavy toll be taken upon our agricultural produce, but our beef and dairy industries would begin to suffer as well. Alfalfa, a flowering plant with genetic ties to hay is the one of the largest sources of nutrition for cattle [2, p. 25]. Incidentally, the massive amount of this product needed to support cattle farms in the US is currently only possible with the pollination of honeybees [2, p. 25]. Without honeybees able to provide this fairly inexpensive source of nutrition, the cost of everything even remotely tied to one of these industries would see a drastic increase in value. Therefore, as the national honeybee population continues to plummet, the more urgent our need becomes to, first of all, find the cause of this problem, and then, to develop a solution.

Every year, beekeepers have become accustomed to a naturally occurring die-off, a term referring to the roughly 17-20% percent of the US's total honeybee population lost each spring due to the frigid winter temperature, common illness, Varroa Destructor mites, or wax moths [2, p. 18]. However, in the time elapsed between 2006 and 2007, beekeepers nationwide began to see a 10% increase in this die-off. Some apiaries (beekeeping facilities) lost up to 95% of their honeybees [2, p. 17]. A documentary presented by the Public Broadcast Station (PBS) calculated that during this time, tens of billions of honeybees perished resulting in an 8 billion to 12 billion dollar effect on the US's agricultural economy [4]. This increase in die-off has been directly tied to CCD.

The next question one might ask is: how was it determined that this phenomenon was something new and not merely an extreme case of the old maladies? In response, Michael Schacker, author of A Spring Without Bees, states that after a colony had collapsed "no adult bees were found in the hives and surprisingly few or no dead bodies were in the hive or on the ground in front of the entrance" [2, p. 15]. Commonly, when a beehive collapses, because of mites or illness, the entrance and the hive itself are littered with honeybee corpses. In contrast, the CCD infected honeybees were healthy enough to fly away from the hive and for whatever reason, failed to return. Schacker also explained that another red flag in the affected bee behavior that signaled CCD was the fact that both other honeybee colonies and predators left all of the honey in collapsed beehives untouched for weeks thereafter [2, p. 16]. In addition, scientists began to notice species of both birds and bats, predators who feed on honeybees, that were experiencing higher death rates than usual, creating a parallel with the honeybee die-off. In 2007, nearly 50% of the national population of common bee-eating bird species had been killed, and the largest die-off of bats ever recorded, a number between 8,000 and 11,000, both happened during the CCD outbreak [2, p. 22].

Many theories have been tested as to what could be causing CCD such as malnutrition, genetically modified crops, climate change, parasites and pathogens, pesticides, and electromagnetic radiation caused by cell phones [5]. However, theories such as malnutrition and genetically modified crops have been ruled out because instances of CCD have been recorded where neither of these effects were present [2, p. 23]. Also, the possibility of pathogens or parasites has also been over ruled. Dr. George Carlo, an American public health scientist declared,

The colony collapse disorder has occurred concurrently on four continents within a very short time frame. If the reason was biological or chemical, there would be a pattern of epidemic spread....we would be able to trace the spread of bee disappearance or Colony Collapse Disorder from a source similar to the spread of SARS a few years ago. That is not the case. The condition has hit each continent at roughly the same time. [6]

Lastly, even though global warming may pose a threat to the surface temperature of the Earth, it has not been seriously discussed as a possible cause of CCD. Consequently, the two largest speculations for the source of the CCD outbreak, currently, are the affect of pesticides and cell phone radiation.

Positions

Due to their genetic composition, honeybees are predisposed to be more susceptible to illness when compared with other bees. Honeybees have a high number of genes dedicated to intelligence, which makes it possible for them to function so efficiently. However, this essential attribute is also one of their biggest downfalls. Since a large portion of their genetic code is dedicated to learning and intellect, other sections, such as immunity and anatomical defense, are not sufficient to provide adequate protection against biological threats [2, p. 6]. Without this protection, the probability that harmful foreign chemicals, such as pesticides, will have negative effects upon the honeybee is immense [2, p. 6]. An article published by the Public Library of Science (PLOS) details a study that found, "Three out of five pollen and wax samples from 23 states had at least one systemic pesticide—a chemical designed to spread throughout all parts of a plant" [7]. Among these pesticides, a particular variant of insecticide called neonicotinoid, a nicotine based toxin that targets the nervous system, was identified as a sizable risk to honeybees. National bee expert Dennis vanEngelsdorp acknowledged that honeybees are dying from something comparable to the human influenza virus [8]. However, the type of sickness has differed in each affected colony [8]. In September of 2009 vanEngelsdorp affirmed, "There's different strains and different types of viruses bees can get. CCD bees have a lot more pathogens than healthy bees do. The question is, why are these bees suddenly so susceptible to these different pathogens?" [8]. According to Rowan Jacobsen, in his book Fruitless Fall, one possible answer to this question is imidacloprid [1, p. 86]. Imidacloprid is a type of neonicotinoid that was proven by studies conducted in Italy, France and the United Kingdom to instigate the exact same CCD symptoms demonstrated in the outbreak of 2006 [1, p. 89]. However, Jeff Pettis, a scientist for the United States Department of Agriculture (USDA) is currently conducting an investigation on the effects of pesticides, including imidacloprid, on honeybee health, and no conclusive data will be released until September 2012 [9]. Consequently, given that pesticides have not yet been identified as the cause of CCD, other suspects, such as electromagnetic radiation, still hold sway.

Cell phones function by emitting short signals in the form of radio-frequency energy waves, which are a type of electromagnetic radiation [10]. According to James Katz, a professor of communication and director of Rutgers University's Center for Mobile Communications Studies, nearly 60% of the entire US population, almost 297 million people, own mobile phones [11]. With over 6 billion people in the world, the total number of cell phone users is colossal, and the amount of electromagnetic radiation is only increasing. Dr. George Carlo, who also headed the Wireless Technology Research program, stated in 2008, "today we have surpassed three billion [cell phones]. That suggests we are near a saturation point of these waves in the ambient environment" [6]. The first evidence of the effect of these waves was discovered when Wolfgang Harst, Jochen Kuhn, and Hermann Stever, all professors at Landau University in Germany, placed cell phones in proximity to honeybee hives and the bees refused to return [12]. In agreement with this study, Carlo believes that Information Carrying Radio Waves (ICRW), the type most prevalent in cell phones, are the culprit for causing CCD [13]. A review of the study at Landau University done by Dr. Ulrich Warnke, from the University of Saarland concludes that the "orientation and navigation of bees may be disturbed by man-made technical communication fields" [13]. The reason honey bees have such an impeccable sense of direction is due to a mineral in their body called magnetite which allows them to navigate by using the Earth's gravitational field [13]. However, when the electromagnetic radiation from cell phones permeates an area inhabited by honeybees, the use of the magnetite with the gravitational fields is disrupted. The possibility that pesticides, cell phones, or possibly both are the cause of CCD is prevalent, however until a complete compilation of all the data is gathered, it will be impossible to conclude exactly what is responsible.

Common Ground

Though supporters of cell phone radiation and pesticide theories may disagree on what is causing the honeybees to disappear, they do agree upon several fronts. Both sides agree that if we do not do anything to prevent the loss of honeybees an agricultural crisis will occur. Also, they agree that the effects of technology are the basis for theories. Our predicament, comparable to the situation Garret Hardin hypothesized in his article, "The Tragedy of the Commons," has reoccurred. A "commons" is defined as an area of resources that are mutually owned by all plants and animals. In this case, our technology is negatively affecting these areas that are also inhabited by honeybees. Our global community, acting collectively, has threatened the livelihood of one of the most invaluable resources that we all share, the honeybee, with the advancement of technology. However both sides also agree that, globally, we need cell phone and pesticide technology to survive. However, as Hardin concluded, "Some social problems have no technical, that is, scientific or technological, solution, but must be addressed by moral and political means" [14]. Unfortunately, CCD may become a social problem, social in terms of the agriculture of the world, which we may not be able to fix by scientific means. If this is the case, it may be possible to counteract the honeybee crisis through politics and a more ethical standard of living. However, as opposed to Hardin's conclusion, before we regulate cell phone production and legislate our use of pesticides, there may still be a technologic solution.

Solution

Although European honeybees are the best at pollinating our flowering plants, they are not the only ones that are capable of meeting the United States' agricultural standards. A strain of Russian bees has shown potential to become a replacement for the CCD prone honeybees in the US [15]. The Russian bees have shown a much higher resistance to the CCD symptoms and also have a 70% overwinter survival rate as opposed to the 50-60% demonstrated by honeybees [15]. Not only would the Russian bees alleviate some of the financial stress that has been applied to American apiaries since they would not have to replace as many bees the following spring, but the Russian bees are almost completely immune to the Varroa mite which almost drove the honeybee to extinction in 1994 [15]. In addition, according to Dr. LeFebvre, a professor at the University of California, Davis, the Russian bees are constantly discarding the weak and sickly bees to keep a strong and healthy colony [15]. In light of this, beehives inhabited with the Russian strain would not only live longer, but would also produce honey and pollinate more efficiently. However, if CCD affects all strains of bees to an irreversible extent, we will need an alternative solution to bee pollination to sustain our agriculture.

If the day comes when the last bee dies, and we have no other alternative, an efficient form of artificial pollination will need to be employed to prevent starvation. Fortunately, successful trials of artificial cross-pollination have already occurred in Thailand. A research team working for the Bangkok Department of Agriculture worked by hand to encourage self-pollination and cross-pollination of the durian tree [16]. The self-pollination (meaning that the stamen, the pollen producer, activates the pistil, the pollen fertilizer, on the same plant) was about as effective as open pollination (pollination by way of the natural environment) and both returned low outputs of fruit [16]. However, when the durian trees were cross-pollinated with other durian cultivars (species of the same family that are bred to emphasize a particular trait in the fruit such as size or color) the output of fruit was greatly increased as well as the fruit's shape and size [16]. Cross-pollination, though tedious and slow, is currently the most promising form of artificial pollination and may serve as a short-term solution in a bee-deprivation period. On the other hand, in order to avoid an agricultural crisis in the first place, a form of beekeeping already in implementation has proven to be the most effective way to further prevent CCD.

Organic beekeeping has thus far proven to be the only section of the honeybee industry that has been unaffected by CCD. First of all, organic beekeepers use smaller brood cells (meaning smaller bees due to a smaller incubation area) to discourage the production of more male honeybees [2, p. 45]. This method has not only proven to have a greater resilience to parasites and infection, but also has insured a higher percentage of healthy genetic code transferred to the offspring when the males mate with the hive queen [2, p. 45]. In contrast with commercial beekeeping, organic beekeepers always use pollen and honey for feeding. Commercial beekeepers, to make the biggest profit, take the honey and pollen out of the hives as soon as they arrive, and replace the nourishment with soy protein and corn syrup. Without the proper sustenance, these commercial honeybees have a higher tendency to become ill and are more susceptible to CCD when the organic honeybees are not. According to Schacker, "Large commercial beekeepers, and most smaller-scale beekeepers, use powerful antibiotics, miticides (which are insecticides) and other toxic chemicals seasonally during the year" [2, p. 15]. With all of these foreign substances introduced into the honeybee's environment, the possibility that misapplication and/or contamination may occur is far greater than what organic honeybees experience [2, p. 15]. However, the greatest difference between commercial and organic beekeeping is that organic honeybees are born and raised away from cell phone towers and pesticide-ridden farms [2, p. 15]. These organic honeybees only pollinate wild flora and have yet to experience any symptoms of CCD. Though this may seem like the ideal solution for the CCD dilemma, it does have one major drawback. If this type of beekeeping were implemented nationwide, commercial beekeepers would initially suffer an immense loss due to the fact that they would need to move their facilities to more organic settings. However, if beekeepers are serious about keeping their business, the organic solution, currently, is the most effective way to save the lives of their bees, and possibly the agricultural economy.

Conclusion

Albert Einstein once said, "If the bee disappears from the surface of the earth, man would have no more than four years to live. No more bees, no more pollination ... no more men!" [17]. It is not difficult to imagine this future considering how much we, as a nation, depend on our agriculture. Whether the cause of CCD is due to cell phone towers or pesticides, the message is clear. If we do not take action now to forestall the extinction of the honeybee, we may not live long enough to find an alternative.

References

[1] R. Jacobsen, *Fruitless Fall: The Collapse of the Honey Bee and the Coming Agricultural Crisis*. New York, New York: Bloomsbury USA, 2008, pp. 1-99.

[2] M. A. Schacker, *A Spring Without Bees: How Colony Collapse Disorder Has Endangered Our Food Supply*. Guilford, Connecticut: The Lyons Press, 2008 pp. 1-67.

[3] National Resource Defense Council, "Helping Honeybees: Pesticides Make it Tough for Pollinators," Opposing Viewpoints, Mar 29, 2010. [Online]. Available: http://wwwlib.murdoch.edu.au/find/citation/ieee.html#Books. [Accessed: April 12, 2010].

[4] Public Broadcast Station, "Silence of the Bees: Impact of CCD on US Agriculture," Public Broadcast Station, Oct 28, 2007. [Online]. Available: http://www.pbs.org/wnet/nature/episodes/silence-of-the-bees/impact-of-ccd-on-us-agriculture/37/. [Accessed: April 12, 2010].

[5] D. Hadley, "10 Possible Causes of Colony Collapse Disorder: Theories Behind the Sudden Disappearance of Honeybee Hives," About.com, 2010. [Online]. Available: http://insects.about.com/od/antsbeeswasps/tp/CausesofCCD.htm. [Accessed: April 12, 2010].

[6] G. Carlo, "Dr Carlo Speaks: Radiation Is Killing the Bees Despite the
    Cell Phone Industry's Disinformation Campaign" In These New
    Times, May 17, 2009. [Online]. Available:
    http://inthesenewtimes.com/2009/05/17/dr-carlo-speaks-
    radiation-is-killing-the-bees-despite-the-cell-phone-industrys-
    disinformation-campaign/. [Accessed: April 12, 2010].

[7] S. Bornstein, G. Burke, "Bee Die-Offs Worsened by Winter,
    Pesticides," *Discovery News*, Mar 24, 2010. [Online]. Available:
    http://news.discovery.com/animals/honeybee-hives-winter-
    pesticides.html. [Accessed: April 12, 2010].

[8] R. Cernansky, "The Uncertain Future of Bees with National Bee
    Expert Dennis vanEngelsdorp," Planet Green, Sept 11, 2009.
    [Online]. Available: http://planetgreen.discovery.com/travel-
    outdoors/bee-expert-talks-bees.html. [Accessed: April 12, 2010].

[9] Agriculture Research Service. "Research Project: Investigation of
    the Effects of Pesticides on Honey Bee Health," United States
    Department of Agriculture, Jun 25, 2009. [Online]. Available:
    http://www.ars.usda.gov/research/projects/projects.htm?ACCN_
    NO=416636. [Accessed: April 12, 2010].

[10] How Stuff Works. "How Cell-phone Radiation Works,"
    HowStuffWorks.com August 8, 2001. [Online]. Available:
    http://www.howstuffworks.com/cell-phone-radiation.htm.
    [Accessed: April 12, 2010].

[11] P. Rauch. "Cell Phone Culture," *MIT Communication Forum*, Nov
    17, 2005. [Online]. Available: http://web.mit.edu/comm-
    forum/forums/cell_phone_culture.htm. [Accessed: April 12,
    2010].

[12] Lean, Geoffrey. Hawcross, Harriet. "Are Mobile Phones Wiping out
    our Bees?" *The Independent*, April 15, 2007. [Online]. Available:
    http://www.independent.co.uk/environment/nature/are-mobile-
    phones-wiping-out-our-bees-444768.html. [Accessed: April 12,
    2010].

[13] Bowling, Milt "Where Have the Birds and Bees Gone?" EMRX, 2008. [Online]. Available: http://www.emrx.org/where-birds-and-bees.html. [Accessed: April 12, 2010].

[14] G. Hardin, "The Tragedy of the Commons," *Science*, vol. 62, pp. 305-312. Dec 1968.

[15] M. L. Shen, "Solutions to Colony Collapse Disorder" COSMOS Cluster 7, Jul 26, 2009. [Online]. Available: http://cosmos.ucdavis.edu/archives/2009/cluster7/SHEN_MARGARET.pdf. [Accessed: April 12, 2010].

[16] C. Honsho, K. Yonemori, S. Somsri,S. Subhadrabandhu, A. Sugiura, "Marked improvement of fruit set in Thai durian by artificial cross-pollination," *Scientia Horticulturae*, Volume 101, Issue 4, Sept 30, 2004, pp. 399-406 [Online]. Available: http://www.sciencedirect.com/science/article/B6TC3-4BWYDYN-1/2/4e282e3409898c3a5c4c3ac51359a829. [Accessed: April 12, 2010].

[17] A. Fowler, "Einstein on Bees," *Global Climate Change*, Feb 27, 2007. [Online]. Available: http://globalclimatechange.wordpress.com/2007/04/20/einstein-on-bees/. [Accessed: April 12, 2010].

Appendix A. Blackboard

Course readings for NHV are distributed through Blackboard, usually as Adobe Acrobat (.pdf) files. Blackboard replaces the published course reader once used in NHV; with that reader, students paid for both publication costs and royalty fees. With Blackboard, the cost to students is significantly less. Making *one* copy of a reading for your use during the semester does not violate copyright or subject you to paying royalties. Do keep in mind, though, that all readings on Blackboard are copyrighted. The following statement applies to all readings:

> This article is copyrighted and may be printed only once and exclusively for use in this class. Do not forward or distribute this electronic file to others, and do not save this file beyond the end of this term. Copying, displaying and distributing copyrighted works may infringe upon the owner's copyright. Students who engage in infringing use of copyrighted works are subject to appropriate disciplinary action, as well as those civil remedies and criminal penalties provided by federal law.

All currently registered CSM students have a Blackboard account. If you have logged on to Blackboard before, use your Slate username and your Blackboard password to log on.

If you've never used Blackboard before, here's how to create a password (or recover the password you've forgotten):

1. Go to Blackboard page: http://blackboard.mines.edu.

2. Click the Login button.

3. Click on the "Forgot password?" link.

4. Follow the prompts so that Blackboard can search for your account.

163

Your Blackboard username is the same as your Slate username. Fields are case-sensitive. Remember to capitalize your first and last names.

5. Blackboard will send email message to your CSM address with a link that will allow you to set a Blackboard password.

After you have a valid password, go to the Blackboard login, click Login, and enter your username and Blackboard password.

Students are automatically enrolled in Blackboard courses. You should see that course listed under "My Courses."

Click on the course name, and main web page for the course will appear. Course readings will be available in the "Course Documents" folder displayed on the left or a sub-folder your instructor has created. If you click on any of the readings, it should display within the Blackboard web interface. To save any of the readings to your computer, right-click on it and then select "Save Target As..." (or a similar option, depending on your browser). In some cases, usually with .pdf documents, you'll have to left-click on the file, let it display as an Adobe Acrobat document in your browser, and then use the "Save a Copy" button to save a copy onto your hard drive.

After a Blackboard session, please remember to log out before closing your browser.

APPENDIX B. TURNITIN

All major papers, as well as other assignments at your instructor's discretion, will be submitted to Turnitin, an originality checking service. It compares student papers against its database of 11 billion web pages, 90 million previously submitted student papers, 12,000 newspapers, magazines, and scholarly journals, and thousands of books. That massive database increases monthly.

Institutions of higher education across the country use Turnitin; you may have been asked to submit papers to Turnitin at your high school. Schools who use Turnitin report an 82% reduction in plagiarism, and that is because Turnitin is very, very good at what it does.

For each paper submitted, Turnitin generates an "Originality Report" that presents the original paper along with the other documents whose phrasing is identical to or very similar to the original. Your instructor may or may not make that report available to you. The report itself means little; if you have a direct quote from a source, Turnitin will flag the similarity between your quote and the source. A properly documented quote is, of course, not plagiarism. Your instructor's evaluation of the Turnitin report is what matters; he or she decides whether there has been plagiarism, intentional or unintentional.

Here's how to get signed up for Turnitin and submit a paper:

1. Go to www.turnitin.com.

2. Click "Create a user profile."

3. The new user wizard will open and walk you through the profile creation process. To create a profile, use the class id and enrollment password for your class.

4. After you create a user profile, go through the standard login process. To login, enter your email address and password. Click "Submit" to open your student homepage.

5. Your class now appears on your homepage. Click on the name of the class to enter your class and access your class portfolio.

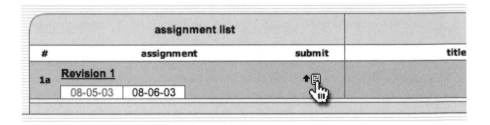

6. You have now opened your class portfolio. Your portfolio shows the assignments your instructor has created. To submit a paper to an assignment, click the submit button.

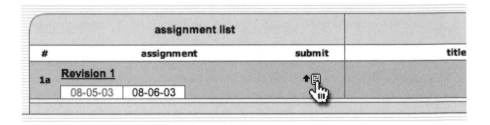

The paper submission page will open. Enter a title for your paper. To select a paper for submission, click on the "browse" button and locate the paper on your computer. Papers can be submitted in MS Word, WordPerfect,

RTF, PDF, PostScript, HTML, and plain text formats. Once you have completed the form, click on the "submit" button.

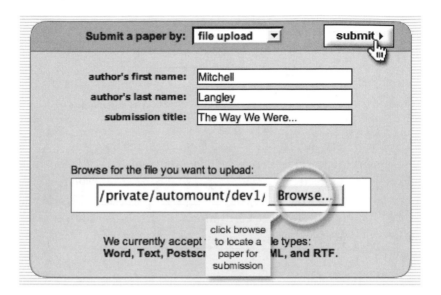

On the following page, look over all the information to double-check that it is correct. If everything is okay, click the "yes, submit" button.

7. After you confirm your submission, a digital receipt will be shown. This receipt will also be sent to you by email. To return to your portfolio and view your submission, click the portfolio button.

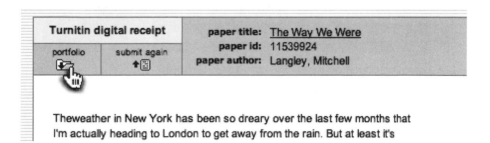

Material adapted from the Turnitin website

Appendix C. Plagiarism

1. CSM Academic Integrity Policy

The faculty, administration and students of the Colorado School of Mines support the principle that all individuals associated with the academic community at CSM have a responsibility for establishing, maintaining and fostering an understanding and appreciation for academic integrity at Mines. This is particularly important in consideration of the unique requirements of an undergraduate education in professional disciplines.

The protection of academic integrity requires clear and consistent standards and definitions, as well as confrontation and sanctions when individuals intentionally violate those standards. The most important of the definitions is that of academic dishonesty— the intentional act of fraud, in which an individual seeks to claim credit for the work and efforts of another without authorization, or uses unauthorized materials or fabricated information in any academic exercise. Academic dishonesty also includes, but is not limited to, forgery of academic documents, intentionally impeding or damaging the academic work of others, or assisting others in acts of academic dishonesty. Some examples of specific acts of academic dishonesty include:

1. Intentionally or knowingly representing the words or ideas of another as one's own in any academic exercise (commonly referred to as "plagiarism"). The following definition of plagiarism has been synthesized and modified from those given in Black's Law Dictionary (1951) and Ballentine's Law Dictionary (1969):

> "Copying or adopting the scientific, literary, musical, or artistic composition or work of another and producing or publishing it as one's own original composition or work. To be liable for

168

'plagiarism' it is not necessary to exactly duplicate another's work: it is sufficient if unfair use of such work is made by lifting of substantial portion thereof, but even an exact counterpart of another's work does not constitute 'plagiarism' if such counterpart was arrived at independently."

2. Intentionally using or attempting to use unauthorized materials, information materials, information or study aids in any academic exercise; e.g. copying from another's examination, looking at notes when specifically instructed to the contrary, or obtaining assistance on a take-home paper or examination when specifically instructed not to do so.

3. Taking material from the library that is there for the use of all students and is not to be removed without permission.

4. Intentionally or knowingly helping or attempting to help another to commit an act of academic dishonesty.

5. Unauthorized use of another's computer program, disk or tape.

If an individual in the CSM academic community becomes aware of an act of academic dishonesty and fails to take appropriate action, the absence of such action threatens the climate of academic integrity at CSM. Such behavior must not be condoned by any member of this community. Appropriate actions include making the other individual aware that his act has been observed, exercising some form of social sanction and reporting the act to individuals in positions of responsibility. Seeking to remain anonymous undermines the integrity of the community and prevents those charged with maintaining standards from doing so.

Inevitably, acts of academic dishonesty will occur. When they do, appropriate members of the academic community must understand and use established procedures for determining the facts and, if there has been academic dishonesty, deciding on the degree of dishonesty and the sanction(s) that should be imposed.

At the Colorado School of Mines, students who observe or are aware of an incident of apparent academic dishonesty should report the matter to a faculty member, the appropriate department head, the Vice President for Student Life, or the Associate Dean of Students. The information is then provided to the faculty member concerned. The faculty member may personally determine whether academic dishonesty has occurred, confront the student(s) with the charge and, if guilt is admitted, impose a sanction such as a grade of zero on a paper or an F in a course, depending on the severity of the offense. All of this information must be transmitted to Associate Dean of Students Office.

If, after confrontation, the student does not admit to committing the offense, the charges and evidence is submitted to the Student Judicial Panel through the Associate Dean of Students Office for resolution. In most cases, substantiated charges of academic dishonesty will result in a grade of F in the course. However, in consultation with the faculty member, a lesser penalty may be assessed. In cases where no penalty is assessed, the faculty member has the option of not reporting the incident to the Vice President. In instances where a penalty is imposed, however, the Associate Dean of Students office must be notified for recording on the official institutional record. As a general rule, the presumptive disciplinary action in serious instances or second offenses is an F in the course, suspension and a notation of same on the student's transcript; the burden of convincing the Vice President that there are specific and significant mitigating factors which should result in a lesser penalty is the student's. Students charged with academic dishonesty must be afforded a fair opportunity for a defense. Upon notification of a finding of academic dishonesty and the associated penalties, the student may appeal the decision, in writing. This written appeal must be made within five school days after the student receives the decision letter. The appeal will be heard by the Student Affairs committee.

2.   WHAT'S PLAGIARISM?

You know what it is. Plagiarism is taking someone else's work and presenting it as your own. It is intellectual theft. The test for plagiarism is simple: "Who really did the work here?" The work includes thought, observation, data, facts—any form of content. The work also includes words, phrases, and sentences—the expression of that content. If you take the content or the expression (or both) from someone else with proper attribution, you are stealing. Here's another way to test for plagiarism: "If I had that thought and wrote that sentence, and if I read *this*, would I feel that someone had stolen from me?" If the answer is "Yes," you have almost certainly plagiarized.

If you take content of any sort from a source, you have to document that content according to either the MLA or IEEE documentation system. The reader must be able to clearly identify where material taken from a source begins and where it ends in your paragraph.

3.   HOW CAN I TELL IF I'VE PLAGIARIZED?

Here's a passage from a published essay:

"Environmentalists so often seem self-righteous, privileged, and arrogant because they so readily consent to identifying nature with play and making it by definition a place where leisured humans come only to visit and not to work, stay, or live. Thus environmentalists have much to say about nature and play and little to say about nature and work."

>   --Richard White, "'Are You an Environmentalist, or
> Do You Work for a Living': Work and Nature"

Here are five efforts at paraphrase:

>   1. According to Richard White, environmentalists seem
>   self-righteous because they identify nature with play and
>   make it a place where people come only to visit and not to
>   work, stay, or live. He notes that environmentalists have
>   lots to say about nature and play and not much to say
>   about nature and work (62).
>
>   2. White feels that we should identify nature with play and
>   make it a place where people come to visit and not to
>   work. He has much to say and about nature and play and
>   little to say about nature and work (62).
>
>   3. For White, nature-lovers are proud, superior, and
>   bigheaded because they happily link the natural world

with leisure and see it as a location where people with time on their hands come to hang out for a while and not to labor, remain, or exist (62).

4. White thinks that environmentalists talk a lot about how nature connects with play but not about how nature connects with work because they arrogantly make nature a place where people on vacation come only to visit and not to live in (62).

In each one, White is given credit for the observation. At the end of each paraphrase, there is a citation in MLA format. But every sentence is clearly based on White's sentence. #1 steals phrasing directly from White. #2 takes phrases directly from White and, at the same time, manages to misrepresent White's thought. #3 simply inserts synonyms. #4 merely rearranges the phrases. In all cases, White did most of the work of writing the sentence. Even though White's name is mentioned and a citation appears at the end, **all four efforts at paraphrase are plagiarism.**

The language of the paraphrase must be completely independent of the original sentence or sentences. The paraphrase must be entirely the work of the person writing it.

4.   PENALTIES

Colorado School of Mines policy defines plagiarism as follows: "Copying or adopting the scientific, literary, musical, or artistic composition or work of another and producing or publishing it as one's own original composition or work. To be liable for 'plagiarism' it is not necessary to exactly duplicate another's work: it is sufficient if unfair use of such work is made by lifting of substantial portion thereof, but even an exact counterpart of another's work does not constitute 'plagiarism' if such counterpart was arrived at independently."

The LAIS plagiarism policy requires these penalties:

- For a first offense, the student will receive an F in the course, and the Vice President for Student Life and Dean of Students will be notified.

- For a second offense, the student will also receive an F in the course and further action, normally suspension from CSM, will be taken by the Vice President for Student Life and Dean of Students. The incident will also become a permanent part of the student's transcript.

Students will submit all major papers and, at instructor discretion, other coursework to Turnitin.com, an anti-plagiarism web service that compares a paper to other papers written at CSM and other schools, to a very large number of websites, and to papers-for-sale. The service flags cases of plagiarism and reports the source or sources.

The penalties for plagiarism are severe. You will spend time in seminar learning how to write a good paraphrases and avoid unintentional plagiarism, how to give credit to your sources by using MLA or IEEE documentation systems. If you need help with an assignment, don't hesitate to ask your instructor. NHV instructors are happy to sit down with you and spend some time talking about the assignment or reviewing a draft. You can also go to the Writing Center (see Appendix E).

Appendix D. NHV Policies

1. Absences

NHV students may miss four class hours without automatic penalty, though missing classes for any reason is discouraged. Your course grade will be lowered by one full letter grade for every absence after those four hours. Every three tardies are equivalent to one absence. If you do miss a class, it's your responsibility to find out from the instructor or your classmates what happened in class and what assignments were made. However, making up assignments does not substitute for your attendance in class

2. Revisions

The secret to good writing is rewriting. You should take each of the major papers through several drafts, revising carefully at each stage. The paper you submit to your instructor at the due date should represent your best work.

NHV policy allows for paper revision after your instructor has assigned a grade if sufficient time remains in the semester. The final grade will be the average of the original paper grade and the grade for the revised paper.

3.   EMAIL

The best and quickest way to communicate with your instructor outside of class is through email. The Blackboard system allows your instructor to send email to all students enrolled in his or her section, and he or she may use this feature to send out reminders of assignments. Get in the habit of checking your Mines email regularly. The world now runs on email; if you're not in the habit of reading email at least once a day, develop the habit now.

When you email your instructor, you are engaging in professional communication. Make sure the subject line clearly indicates the topic of the email. Observe proper grammar, punctuation, and capitalization in the body of the email. Informal tone is perfectly acceptable, but keep in mind that, in email as in other communication, you are presenting yourself to a reader. "Hey, prof, can u resend that signment thing" tells the person reading the email that you are not to be taken seriously.

APPENDIX E. THE WRITING CENTER

The Writing Center is an important resource for students at all stages in the writing process. Call 303.273.3085 to make an appointment to meet with a writing advisor in the Writing Center, located in 309 Stratton Hall. When you go for your appointment, bring the paper assignment sheet and a draft of the paper. Your instructor can tell you the days and hours the Writing Center is open for the current semester.

The Writing Center is open to everyone in the CSM community. After completing NHV, you can make an appointment at the Writing Center for help with assignments in other courses.

Special assistance for students whose native language is not English is available on certain days; call the Writing Center to find out when. An International Conversation Group meets regularly in 410 Stratton Hall to provide practice in conversational English. Ask your instructor for the times and days.

APPENDIX F. GLOSSARY

Aristotle (384 BC -322 BC), one of the great thinkers of Western philosophy, was Plato's student and the teacher of Alexander the Great. Aristotle links ethics with virtue and argues that one cannot study ethics and virtue, but be virtuous and perform virtuous acts. The ultimate goal of virtue ethics, Aristotle contends, is happiness (*eudaimonia*, "living well").

Consequentialism states that the moral value of an action depends on its results. If an action has good results, then individuals should pursue it; if an action has bad results, then it is wrong and it should not be considered.

Deontology (*Deontos* in Greek means "duty") attempts to value an ethical action as right or wrong in itself. According to deontological theory, some actions are right because they are associated with the right rules, so it is our duty to follow on these actions. For instance, telling the truth is always right independent of the consequences.

Ecosystem is an ecological community which functions as a unit together with its environment.

Kant, Immanuel (1724-1804) is a German philosopher of late Enlightenment who produced works relevant to law, religion, history, and ethics and, thus, has been regarded as one of the most influential thinkers of the Western world. In his prominent study, *Critique of Pure Reason*, Kant points out the structure and limitations of reason and argues that human knowledge relies on *a priori* judgments which are possible only when the mind determines the conditions of its own experience. Deontological theory was developed by Kant, who, unlike Mill, contends that a moral action is not defined in terms of its consequences, but in terms of the inner nature of the intention that governs it.

Leopold, Aldo (1887-1948) is an American environmentalist who is considered the father of wildlife management. He developed modern environmental and land ethics.

Mill, John Stuart (1806-1873) is an eighteenth-century British philosopher who became a well-known representative of utilitarianism and consequentialism. Mill also wrote about the liberty of the individual against what he called "the tyranny of the majority" and advocated freedom of speech.

Moral Absolutism refers to moral codes that are absolute and unchangeable.

Moral Dilemma refers to a situation in which the individual is faced with two conflicting courses of action that appear ethical.

Moral Relativism involves the belief that moral codes are changeable and arbitrary depending on time, place, and individual behavior.

Teleology (*Telos* in Greek means "end") implies that any kind of development, whether it is in history, nature, or technology, progresses toward a final end.

Utilitarianism is the form of consequentialism. In his 1863 book, *Utilitarianism*, John Stuart Mill postulates his famous "greatest happiness principle" which means the greatest happiness for the greatest number.

Virtue Ethics evaluates actions in terms of the virtues of the person who performs them. If a person is virtuous and honorable, then his/her actions are supposedly good.

ABOUT THE AUTHORS

Paula Farca received her PhD and a second MA from Oklahoma State University and an MA and BA from West University of Timisoara, Romania. Her research focuses on contemporary and postcolonial literature. Paula published journal articles on southern, Indigenous, and contemporary literature, co-edited an anthology, and is working on a study on Indigenous literature. Paula has been teaching literature and writing to college students for more than ten years. Since 2008, when she joined LAIS, she has taught Nature and Human Values and tried to introduce future engineers to the joy and intellectual excitement of reading and writing.

Cortney Holles is an Instructor in LAIS who has taught Nature and Human Values for 6 years and has enjoyed developing the course focus and material over that time. She began her education with a brief stint as a pre-med major, following her love of math and science, then quickly transferred to her other love—reading—and became an English major. She received her Master of Arts in English from University of Northern Colorado and shortly after began teaching at Mines, a perfect fit for both sides of her brain.

Shira Richman has published fiction, non-fiction, poetry, and interviews in *Third Coast, PopMatters, Spoon River Poetry Review, Willow Springs*, the Seattle Metro buses, and elsewhere. She has been the recipient of City College New York's Raymond Patterson Award and has won Richard Hugo House's New Works Competition. For over seven years she has taught writing in a variety of places including the Juvenile Detention Center in Seattle and a public high school in the Bronx. The most enjoyable teaching she has done, though, is at the Colorado School of Mines.